Beginnings and Endings

Arthur Daigon
Professor of English Education
University of Connecticut

Mimi Schmitt
The High School in the Community
New Haven, Connecticut

Prentice-Hall, Inc.
Englewood Cliffs, New Jersey

Acknowledgments

"The Creation, a Negro Sermon" by James Weldon Johnson from *God's Trombones* by James Weldon Johnson. Copyright 1927 by The Viking Press, Inc. © renewed 1955 by Grace Nail Johnson. All rights reserved. Reprinted by permission of The Viking Press, Inc., 10. "Budget Planet" by Robert Sheckley. Copyright © 1968 by Mercury Press, Inc. Reprinted by permission of The Sterling Lord Agency, Inc., 13. Excerpts from pp. 5-6, *Brave New World* by Aldous Huxley, Copyright 1932 by Aldous Huxley. Reprinted by permission of Harper and Row, Inc., 18. Reprinted by permission of G. P. Putnam's Sons: from *The Once and Future King* by T. H. White. Copyright © 1958 by T. H. White, 20. "What the (Continued on page 155)

Beginnings and Endings
Arthur Daigon and Mimi Schmitt

Designed by Madeline Bastis & Friends

ISBN 0-13-073981-2

10 9 8 7 6 5 4 3 2 1

PRENTICE-HALL INTERNATIONAL, INC., London
PRENTICE-HALL OF AUSTRALIA, PTY. LTD., Sydney
PRENTICE-HALL OF CANADA, LTD., Toronto
PRENTICE-HALL OF INDIA PRIVATE LTD., New Delhi
PRENTICE-HALL OF JAPAN, INC., Tokyo

Contents

In the beginning these four—earth, air, fire and water—formed the vital partnership from which life was born.

In the beginning . . . the surface of the earth had not appeared. There was only calm sea and the great expanse of the sky.

Popol Vuh

1 The Beginning of the World

Have you ever gazed up at the stars and wondered if there is an end to the sky? With so many stars stretching across the sky, it seems as if there could be no end to it all. But have you ever asked yourself, if there is an end to the sky, what could possibly be beyond that? And how did the end come to be or not to be there?

Across the entire face of the earth, human beings have always wondered how the heavens and earth came into being. The next few pages present some differing points of view on the beginning of the world, but there is room in this book for only a few. To add to these, form a small group with some classmates to make up an original creation story to share with the class. Jot down some notes about how you would go about creating a universe if you could do so. What would your ideal universe be like? How many suns would you create and how many planets capable of sustaining life? What would the earth be like? How many continents? What kind of weather? How large would the oceans be? Would there be oceans? What would the people be like and how would they live?

Elect one member of the group to be spokesperson and another to record your ideas on the blackboard. After all the groups have listed their thoughts, discuss each group's ideas to determine what features are common to all.

The best-known account of creation
in the Western world is the Biblical one
from the Book of Genesis. No other
description has such authority; no other
has influenced the course of religious,
moral, scientific, and artistic thought
for thousands of years.

FROM Genesis 1, 2:1-3

In the beginning God created the heavens and the earth. The earth was without form and void, and darkness was upon the face of the deep; and the Spirit of God was moving over the face of the waters.

And God said, "Let there be light"; and there was light. And God saw that the light was good; and God separated the light from the darkness. God called the light Day, and the darkness he called Night. And there was evening and there was morning, one day.

And God said, "Let there be a firmament in the midst of the waters, and let it separate the waters from the waters." And God made the firmament and separated the waters which were under the firmament from the waters which were above the firmament. And it was so. And God called the firmament Heaven. And there was evening and there was morning, a second day.

And God said, "Let the waters under the heavens be gathered together into one place, and let the dry land appear." And it was so. God called the dry land Earth, and the waters that were gathered together he called Seas. And God saw that it was good. And God said, "Let the earth put forth vegetation, plants yielding seed, and fruit trees bearing fruit in which is their seed, each according to its kind, upon the earth." And it was so. The earth brought forth vegetation, plants yielding seed according to their own kinds, and trees bearing fruit in which is their seed, each according to its kind. And God saw that it was good. And there was evening and there was morning, a third day.

And God said, "Let there be lights in the firmament of the heavens to separate the day from the night; and let them be for signs and for seasons and for days and years, and let them be lights in the firmament of the heavens to give light upon the earth." And it was so. And God made the two great lights, the greater light to rule the day, and the lesser light to rule the night; he made the stars also. And God set them in the firmament of the heavens to give light upon the earth, to rule over the day and over the night, and to separate the light from the darkness. And God saw that it was good. And there was evening and there was morning, a fourth day.

And God said, "Let the waters bring forth swarms of living creatures, and let birds fly above the earth across the firmament of the heavens." So God created the great sea monsters and every

living creature that moves, with which the waters swarm, according to their kinds, and every winged bird according to its kind. And God saw that it was good. And God blessed them, saying, "Be fruitful and multiply and fill the waters in the seas, and let birds multiply on the earth." And there was evening and there was morning, a fifth day.

And God said, "Let the earth bring forth living creatures according to their kinds: cattle and creeping things and beasts of the earth according to their kinds." And it was so. And God made the beasts of the earth according to their kinds and the cattle according to their kinds, and everything that creeps upon the ground according to its kind. And God saw that it was good.

Then God said, "Let us make man in our image, after our likeness; and let them have dominion over the fish of the sea, and over the birds of the air, and over the cattle, and over all the earth, and over every creeping thing that creeps upon the earth." So God created man in his own image, in the image of God he created him; male and female he created them. And God blessed them, and God said to them, "Be fruitful and multiply, and fill the earth and subdue it; and have dominion over the fish of the sea and over the birds of the air and over every living thing that moves upon the earth." And God said, "Behold, I have given you every plant yielding seed which is upon the face of all the earth, and every tree with seed in its fruit; you shall have them for food. And to every beast of the earth, and to every bird of the air, and to everything that creeps on the earth, everything that has the breath of life, I have given every green plant for food." And it was so. And God saw everything that he had made, and behold, it was very good. And there was evening and there was morning, a sixth day.

Thus the heavens and the earth were finished, and all the host of them. And on the seventh day God finished his work which he had done, and he rested on the seventh day from all his work which he had done. So God blessed the seventh day and hallowed it, because on it God rested from all his work which he had done in creation.

The Bible is very precise about the order in which God created the heavens and earth. List in order exactly what was created on each day.

This "Song of Creation" from the
Rig-Veda (a Hindu sacred book of over
1,000 psalms) is more than 3,000 years
old. Presuming that no one can know
for sure how the creation occurred, it
uses opposites and questions to explain
the beginning of the world.

Song of Creation

In the beginning there was neither non-being nor being—
There was no region of air nor any sky beyond it.
What did it cover? and where? and what protected it?
Was there water, deep and unfathomable?

In the beginning there was no death nor anything immortal.
There was no division between day and night.
The One*, by Itself, breathed without breathing,
And nothing whatsoever existed apart from it.

There was darkness concealed in darkness
And the entire world was surging chaos.
Everything was empty and without form,
And from the mighty power of warmth was born the One. . . .

Who knows for sure and could here declare
Whence creation was born and whence it flows?
Only after the creation do the gods exist,
So who then can know where it began?

He alone, the Overseer, in the highest heaven knows
Where this flowing began,
Or whether He formed it or not—
He knows for sure, or perhaps He does not!

According to both the Book of Genesis and the "Song of Creation," the world was without form in the beginning. Write a description of this state, as you imagine it might have been, by comparing it to something in our present world which we all understand.

* a term meaning *God*

6

First there was Chaos
The vast immeasurable Abyss
Outrageous as a sea,
Dark, wasteful, wild.

John Milton

A scientific explanation of the beginning of the earth, solar system, or universe does not necessarily deny that a God was involved in creation. However, scientists primarily base their theories on the laws of nature as they understand them to exist instead of on faith. Scientific points of view differ just as religious and mythical explanations of creation differ.

Scientific Theory

Where did the earth come from according to scientific theory? There are two popular theories about *the origin of the solar system:*

Laplace's Nebular Hypothesis

The solar system started as a huge, rotating cloud of gas and dust which gradually cooled and shrank, taking the shape of a sphere with a fat middle. This mid-section bulge spun off into space as the sphere rotated faster and faster. The bulge formed new planets which cooled and shrank as they traveled around the sphere which became the sun of our solar system.

The Moulton-Chamberlin Planetesimal Theory

This theory is an example of the Collision and Tidal Effect. The solar system began when a star approached the sun and pulled from it masses of gas and dust. The gases, floating in space, cooled and formed small solid masses called planetesimals, which were then drawn together to form the planets.

The origin of the earth in either case is basically the same. The planet gradually condensed from a mass of gas and dust which was at first probably quite cold. Then, as the sun warmed up and radioactive decay in the earth set in, the temperature on earth rose, until the planet became semi-molten. Scientists divide the history of the earth into five great eras: Archaeozoic, Proterozoic, Palaeozoic, Mesozoic, and Cenozoic, of which only the last three contain any appreciable record of animal life.

Scientists usually go one step farther and ask themselves where the universe came from. Here are some of their theories:

The Expanding Universe Theory

According to some scientists the whole universe was once packed together in one tight little ball which exploded and began to expand. As it expanded the stars and galaxies were formed, including our earth. Since it is still expanding, according to this theory, the stars and galaxies are moving farther and farther apart. Eventually, we people on earth will be

At eighteen, I thought that the theory presented in our astronomy class was the 'truth' and that my friend's belief, the Biblical one, was mere fantasy. It should have given me pause, however, that the theory propounded in college was not the one I had learned in high school, only three or four years earlier. My high school teacher told us about the Laplace nebular hypothesis to account for the origin of the earth and the solar system; whereas now, in college, I was being given the Chamberlin-Mounton [sic.] planetesimal hypothesis.

Philip Freund

Dust and gases begin to condense . . .

. . . and by accumulation the planet is formed but the planet is still cold

able to see only those stars which are closest to us, and finally, no stars at all!

The Pulsating Model

Some scientists disagree with the theory that the universe will go on expanding forever. These scientists believe that the rate of expansion will slow down as the pull of gravity between galaxies works in opposition to the force of expansion. Eventually, according to this theory, the pull of gravity will overcome the force of expansion and the universe will shrink back into a primeval nucleus. Then the process will repeat itself.

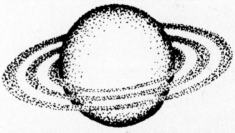

Then radioactive decay begins to heat up the earth . . .

The Steady State Theory

This theory holds that the universe had no beginning and will have no end. There is only hydrogen in the space between galaxies, according to this theory, which is being created all the time at a very slow rate. This hydrogen eventually forms clusters of galaxies which expand, age and die, but the universe always has the same density; only the parts within it can be created and destroyed.

Until it is a semi-molten body

Your younger brother or sister has asked you for a scientific explanation of how the world began. Write a summary of what you have just read so that a small child would be able to understand it.

Like the "Song of Creation" from the
Rig-Veda, the Biblical account of
creation is thousands of years old.
When the writer of Genesis began his
task, he wrote so that the Hebrew tribes
would easily be able to understand
the sacred scriptures. The poem that
follows is called "A Negro Sermon"; in
it, the poet has changed the style of
the Biblical account to suit his own
special audience.

The Creation, A Negro Sermon

James Weldon Johnson

And God stepped out on space,
And he looked around and said,
"I'm lonely—
I'll make me a world."

And far as the eye of God could see
Darkness covered everything,
Blacker than a hundred midnights
Down in a cypress swamp.

Then God smiled,
And the light broke,
And the darkness rolled up on one side,
And the light stood shining on the other,
And God said, *"That's good!"*

Then God reached out and took the light in
    His hands,
And God rolled the light around in His hands,
Until He made the sun;
And He set that sun a-blazing in the heavens.
And the light that was left from making the sun
God gathered up in a shining ball
And flung against the darkness,
Spangling the night with the moon and stars.

Then down between
The darkness and the light
He hurled the world;
And God said, *"That's good!"*

Then God himself stepped down—
And the sun was on His right hand,
And the moon was on His left;
The stars were clustered about His head,
And the earth was under His feet.
And God walked, and where He trod
His footsteps hollowed the valleys out
And bulged the mountains up.

Then He stopped and looked and saw
That the earth was hot and barren.
So God stepped over to the edge of the world
And He spat out the seven seas;
He batted His eyes, and the lightnings flashed;
He clapped His hands, and the thunders rolled;
And the waters above the earth came down,
The cooling waters came down.

Then the green grass sprouted,
And the little red flowers blossomed,
The pine-tree pointed his finger to the sky,
And the oak spread out his arms;
The lakes cuddled down in the hollows of the ground,
And the rivers ran down to the sea;
And God smiled again,
And the rainbow appeared,
And curled itself around His shoulder.

Then God raised His arm and He waved His hand
Over the sea and over the land,
And He said, *"Bring forth! Bring forth!"*
And quicker than God could drop His hand,
Fishes and fowls
And beast and birds
Swam the rivers and the seas,
Roamed the forests and the woods,
And split the air with their wings,
And God said, *"That's good!"*

Then God walked around
And God looked around
On all that He had made.
He looked at His sun,
And He looked at His moon,
And He looked at His little stars;
He looked on His world
With all its living things,
And God said, *"I'm lonely still."*

Then God sat down
On the side of a hill where He could think;
By a deep, wide river He sat down;
With His head in His hands,
God thought and thought,
Till He thought, *"I'll make me a man!"*

Up from the bed of the river
God scooped the clay;
And by the bank of the river
He kneeled Him down;
And there the great God Almighty,
Who lit the sun and fixed it in the sky,
Who flung the stars to the most far corner
      of the night,
Who rounded the earth in the middle of
      His hand—
This Great God,
Like a mammy bending over her baby,
Kneeled down in the dust
Toiling over a lump of clay
Till He shaped it in His own image;

Then into it He blew the breath of life,
And man became a living soul.
Amen. Amen.

**Compare the sequence of events in this poem with
the outline of events in Genesis that you have written.
Next, write a paragraph in which you compare and
contrast this poem with the Genesis account in terms
of mood, style, and the effects on the reader or
listener.**

God has often been called the Architect of the Universe. The author of the following humorous story has taken that title literally: the architect has gone to a contractor to have his planet built. As in some contracting, the customer is not satisfied with the finished product.

Budget Planet

Robert Sheckley

I was still quite a small contractor then. I put up a planet here and there, and I got to do an occasional dwarf star. But jobs were always hard to come by, and the customers were invariably capricious, faultfinding, and slow in their payments. Customers were hard to please in those days; they argued about every little detail. *Change this, change that, why must water flow downhill, the gravity's too heavy, the hot air rises when it ought to fall.* And so forth.

I was quite naive in those days. I used to explain the esthetic and practical reasons for everything I did. Before long, the questions and the explanations were taking longer than the jobs. There was entirely too much talk-talk. I knew that I had to do something about it, but I couldn't figure out what.

Then, just before the Earth project, a whole new approach to customer relations began to shape itself in my mind. I found myself muttering to myself, "Form follows function." I liked the way it sounded. But then I would ask myself, *"Why* must form follow function?" And the reason I gave myself was, "Form follows function because that is an immutable* law of nature and one of the fundamental axioms of applied science." I liked the sound of that, too, although it didn't make much sense.

But sense didn't matter. What mattered was that I had made a new discovery. I had unwittingly stumbled into the art of advertising and salesmanship, and I had discovered the gimmick of great possibilities: Namely, the doctrine of scientific determinism. Earth was my first test case, and that is why I will always remember it.

A tall, bearded old man with piercing eyes had come to me and ordered a planet. (That was how your planet began, Carmody.) Well, I did the job quickly, in six days I believe, and thought that would be the end of it. It was another of those budget planets, and I had cut a few corners here and there. But to hear the

* unchanging

AS IS

"And you've filled what little land you gave me with deserts and swamps and jungles and mountains."

"It's scenic," I pointed out.

"I don't care from scenic!" the fellow thundered. "Oh, sure, one ocean, a dozen lakes, a couple rivers, one or two mountain ranges, that would have been fine. Dresses the place up, gives the inhabitants a good feeling. But what you gave me is *shlock!*"

"There's a reason for it," I said. In point of fact, we couldn't make the job pay except by using reconstituted mountains, a lot of rivers and oceans as filler, and a couple of deserts I had bought cheap from Ourie the planet-junker. But I wasn't going to tell *him* that.

"A reason!" he screamed. "What will I tell my people? I'm putting an entire race on that planet, maybe two or three. They'll be humans, made in my own image, and humans are notoriously picky, just as I am. What am I supposed to tell them?"

Well, I knew what he could tell them, but I didn't want to be offensive; so I pretended to give the matter some thought. And strangely enough, I *did* think. And I came up with the gimmick to end all gimmicks.

"You just tell them the plain scientific truth," I said. "You tell them that, scientifically, everything that *is* must be."

owner complain, you'd have thought I had stolen the eyes out of his head.

"Why are there so many tornadoes?" he asked.

"It's part of the atmosphere circulation system," I told him. Actually, I had been a little rushed at that time; I had forgotten to put in an air circulation overload valve.

"Three quarters of the place is water!" he told me. "And I clearly specified a 4 to 1 land-to-water ratio!"

"Well, we couldn't do it that way!" I said to him. I had lost his ridiculous specifications; I never can keep track of these absurd little one-planet projects.

The contractor has hired you to write blurbs to promote his Budget Planet as a desirable place to live. The contractor has already cleverly explained that tornadoes are part of the "atmosphere circulation system." Think of similar clever explanations for the smells, sights, and sounds of earth (or absence of them) that may impress a prospective customer.

14

1. Find a real creation story to contribute to a class Myth Book.

2. In a science book, look up the order of creation according to scientific theory and compare that order to the one in Genesis. Prepare a short oral report on your findings and, if possible, accompany your report with artists' conceptions of the creation.

3. Using drawings or photographs from magazines, prepare an illustrated version of the creation story from either Genesis or the Rig-Veda.

4. Examine carefully the scientific theories of the origins of the solar system and the universe. Using the diagram of the origin of the earth (p. 9) as a model, draw a sketch of your own to illustrate one of the five theories.

5. "The Creation" by James Weldon Johnson was written in the style of a Negro sermon. Write your own creation poem for a particular audience. For example, if you choose to address your poem to sailors, you should keep in mind details of the creation that would appeal particularly to sailors.

6. After reading "Budget Planet," decide whether you think the earth is a budget model or a deluxe one. Working with a partner, design a complete sales brochure to promote the earth as the perfect place for creatures to decide to settle. Promote it either as economy-budget-priced for the economy-minded or high-priced for those who can afford to be different.

7. Write up the news story of the exciting discovery of a new planet from the point of view of a roving, interplanetary reporter who writes for the *Galactic Gazette*. The reporter has just returned from an exploratory space trip where he has seen with his own eyes the creation of a new planet which is being called earth.

Activities

8. On a 3 x 5 card or on a half sheet of paper, write your own personal definition of God. Do not sign it. When all the definitions have been collected, form a committee to tabulate the results to determine similar and varying beliefs of the class members. The committee should draw a graph of the results and present their findings to the class.

9. Make up a tale to explain a natural phenomenon, such as why the sea is salty, why the sky is blue, or why there are tides.

10. In response to the accounts of how the world began which you have read in this chapter, role-play one of the following people in a panel discussion about how the world began. Study the selections carefully, as well as the point of view of the person you represent, so that you can react easily and realistically.

(a) a priest, minister, or rabbi
(b) a scientist
(c) an agnostic (a person who believes that the human mind cannot know whether there is a God or not)
(d) a fundamentalist (a person who believes in the exact words of the Bible)
(e) a poet
(f) a science fiction writer

2
The Origins of the Species

The course of human civilization can be traced back thousands of years. At Jericho, for example, walls and other artifacts have been unearthed that archaeologists say are over 8,000 years old. Cave paintings in France and Spain hint at how human beings lived around 15,000 years ago. But where were human beings before the earliest signs of their existence? Was there a moment in time when a Creator said, "Let there be human beings"? Or, as scientists theorize, did we evolve into our present forms over a period of millions of years? Explore these possibilities by gathering folk tales, religious writings, and myths explaining the origins of the first man and woman. Bring the story to class and copy appropriate ones to include in the class Myth Book.

Three forces have made possible the evolvement of living things: time, radiation and that invention, death.
Robert Ardrey

Will humankind someday be able to play creator to form a new human species? In Aldous Huxley's science fiction novel *Brave New World,* future society maintains itself by guaranteeing the conformity of all its members. Families no longer have children. Instead, babies are formed in test-tubes and are bred to perform only one particular task in their lives. Through a process called *bokanovskification,* up to ninety-six babies can be formed from one human egg—all identical in every detail. In the following excerpt, the Director of Hatcheries and Conditioning (D.H.C.) is giving a tour to a group of students.

FROM Brave New World

Aldous Huxley

"Bokanovsky's Process," repeated the Director, and the students underlined the words in their little notebooks.

One egg, one embryo, one adult— normality. But a bokanovskified egg will bud, will proliferate, will divide. From eight to ninety-six buds, and every bud will grow into a perfectly formed embryo, and every embryo into a full-sized adult. Making ninety-six human beings grow where only one grew before. Progress.

"Essentially," the D.H.C. concluded, "bokanovskification consists of a series of arrests of development. We check the normal growth and, paradoxically enough, the egg responds by budding."

Responds by budding. The pencils were busy.

He pointed. On a very slowly moving band a rack-full of test-tubes was entering a large metal box, another rack-full was emerging. Machinery faintly purred. It took eight minutes for the tubes to go through, he told them. Eight minutes of hard X-rays being about as much as an egg can stand. A few died; of the rest, the least susceptible divided into two; most put out four buds; some eight; all were returned to the incubators, where the buds began to develop; then, after two days, were suddenly chilled, chilled and checked. Two, four, eight, the buds in their turn budded; and having budded were dosed almost to death with alcohol; consequently burgeoned[1] again and having budded—bud out of bud out of bud— were thereafter—further arrest being generally fatal—left to develop in peace. By which time the original egg was in a fair way to becoming anything from eight to ninety-six embryos—a prodigious improvement, you will agree, on nature.

[1] developed rapidly

18

Identical twins—but not in piddling twos and threes as in the old viviparous[2] days, when an egg would sometimes accidentally divide; actually by dozens, by scores at a time.

"Scores," the Director repeated and flung out his arms, as though he were distributing largesse.[3] "Scores."

But one of the students was fool enough to ask where the advantage lay.

"My good boy!" The Director wheeled sharply round on him. "Can't you see? Can't you *see?*" He raised a hand; his expression was solemn. "Bokanovsky's Process is one of the major instruments of social stability!"

Major instruments of social stability.

Standard men and women; in uniform batches. The whole of a small factory staffed with the products of a single bokanovskified egg.

"Ninety-six identical twins working ninety-six identical machines!" The voice was almost tremulous[4] with enthusiasm. "You really know where you are. For the first time in history." He quoted the planetary motto. "Community, Identity, Stability." Grand words. "If we could bokanovskify indefinitely the whole problem would be solved."

You are one of the observers on the tour taking notes on the Bokanovsky process. You represent a head of state who is interested in "maintaining social stability." Prepare a detailed written report on how the process works.

---

[2] bearing living young

[3] gifts given in a generous and showy way

[4] trembling

Compared to other animals, we have few defenses against nature — no fur, no wings, no fins, no claws. In the following tale, young King Arthur (called Wart) is being instructed by an animal (the badger) on how humankind came to be so defenseless.

FROM The Once and Future King

T. H. White

"People often ask, as an idle question, whether the process of evolution began with the chicken or the egg. Was there an egg out of which the first chicken came, or did a chicken lay the first egg? I am in a position to say that the first thing created was the egg.

"When God had manufactured all the eggs out of which the fishes and the serpents and the birds and the mammals and even the duck-billed platypus would eventually emerge, he called the embryos before Him, and saw that they were good.

"Perhaps I ought to explain," added the badger, lowering his papers nervously and looking at the Wart over the top of them, *"that all embryos look very much the same.* They are what you are before you are born—and, whether you are going to be a tadpole or a peacock or a cameleopard[1] or a man, when you are an embryo you just look like a peculiarly repulsive and helpless human being. I continue as follows:

"The embryos stood in front of God, with their feeble hands clasped politely over their stomachs and their heavy heads hanging down respectfully, and God addressed them.

"He said: 'Now, you embryos, here you are, all looking exactly the same, and We are going to give you the choice of what you want to be. When you grow up you will get bigger anyway, but We are pleased to grant you another gift as well. You may alter any parts of yourselves into anything which you think would be useful to you in later life. For instance, at the moment you cannot dig. Anybody who would like to turn his hands into a pair of spades or garden forks is allowed to do so. Or, to put it another way, at present you can only use your mouths for eating. Anybody who would like to use his mouth as an offensive weapon, can change it by asking, and be a corkindrill or a sabre-toothed tiger. Now then, step up and choose your tools, but remember that what you choose you will grow into, and will have to stick to.'

"All the embryos thought the matter over politely, and then, one by one, they stepped up before the eternal throne. They were allowed two or three specializations, so that some chose to use their

---

[1] early name for the *giraffe*

20

arms as flying machines and their mouths as weapons, or crackers, or drillers, or spoons, while others selected to use their bodies as boats and their hands as oars. We badgers thought very hard and decided to ask three boons. We wanted to change our skins for shields, our mouths for weapons, and our arms for garden forks. These boons were granted. Everybody specialized in one way or another, and some of us in very queer ones. For instance, one of the desert lizards decided to swap his whole body for blotting-paper, and one of the toads who lived in the drouthy antipodes[2] decided simply to be a water-bottle.

"The asking and granting took up two long days—they were the fifth and sixth, so far as I remember—and at the very end of the sixth day, just before it was time to knock off for Sunday, they had got through all the little embryos except one. This embryo was Man.

" 'Well, Our little man,' said God. 'You have waited till the last, and slept on your decision, and We are sure you have been thinking hard all the time. What can We do for you?'

" 'Please God,' said the embryo, 'I think that You made me in the shape which I now have for reasons best known to Yourselves, and that it would be rude to change. If I am to have my choice I will stay as I am. I will not alter any of the parts which You gave me, for other and doubtless inferior tools, and I will stay a defenceless embryo all my life, doing my best to make myself a few feeble implements out of the wood, iron and the other materials which You have seen fit to put before me. If I want a boat I will try to construct it out of trees, and if I want to fly, I will put together a chariot to do it for me. Probably I have

been very silly in refusing to take advantage of Your kind offer, but I have done my very best to think it over carefully, and now hope that the feeble decision of this small innocent will find favour with Yourselves.'

" 'Well done,' exclaimed the Creator in delighted tones. 'Here, all you embryos, come here with your beaks and whatnots to look upon Our first Man. He is the only one who has guessed Our riddle, out of all of you, and We have great pleasure in conferring upon him the Order of Dominion over the Fowls of the Air, and the Beasts of the Earth, and the Fishes of the Sea. Now let the rest of you get along, and love and multiply, for it is time to knock off for the week-end. As for you, Man, you will be a naked tool all your life, though a user of tools. You will look like an embryo till they bury you, but all the others will be embryos before your might. Eternally undeveloped, you will always remain potential in Our image, able to see some of Our sorrows and to feel some of Our joys. We are partly sorry for you, Man, but partly hopeful. Run along then, and do your best. And listen, Man, before you go . . .'

" 'Well?' asked Adam, turning back from his dismissal.

" 'We were only going to say,' said God shyly, twisting Their hands together. 'Well, We were just going to say, God bless you.' "

You are one of the embryos standing in front of the Creator. Write a formal request, describing the physical characteristics that you would like to be given. In your request, do not name the type of animal, real or imagined, that you would like to be. Exchange requests with your classmates and try to draw what creature is being described.

---

[2] a place on the opposite side of the earth

In the folklore of American Indians, the coyote is the most human of animals, representing the cruel, gluttonous, and lustful side of human nature. On the other hand, the bear represents our good or godlike natures. In this tale from the Miwak tribe, the clever, deceitful coyote has the last word in deciding what human beings will look like.

What the Coyote Made

Barbara Stanford with Gene Stanford

The coyote called a council of animals to decide how man should be made. The mountain lion spoke first. He said, "I think that it is very important for man to have a loud voice like I do. And he might as well also have sharp claws, long fangs, and beautiful hair like I do."

The grizzly bear answered, "One loud voice like yours is all we need in this world. How will we ever have peace if we create another animal as noisy as you! I think men should be nice and quiet like me."

The buck replied, "I agree. He does not need to be able to roar. What he does need is a magnificent head of antlers. He also needs keen eyes and ears."

The coyote then got up and said that they were all stupid. "There is no sense at all," he complained, "in making man if he is going to be just like someone else. We should take the best points from every animal and put them all together. Man could have a loud voice, but should not use it all the time. He should be able to stand upright like the grizzly. He should have eyes and ears like the buck. But most important of all, he should be clever like me!"

But after the coyote spoke, the other animals all started shouting their disagreements and soon were in a fight. Finally everyone sat down by himself and started molding man out of clay. But night came and everyone except the coyote fell asleep. He stayed awake until he was finished and that is why man turned out the way the coyote wanted him to.

Imagine that young King Arthur has been sent to learn the coyote's story about the beginning of the human species. Write the story from the coyote's point of view. Use the first person form and be sure to reveal the coyote's clever and deceitful nature.

. . . But for the man there was not found a helper fit for him. So the LORD God caused a deep sleep to fall upon the man, and while he slept took one of his ribs and closed up its place with flesh;

and the rib which the LORD God had taken from the man he made into a woman and brought her to the man.

Then the man said,

"This at last is bone of my bones and flesh of my flesh;

she shall be called Woman,
because she was taken out of Man."

Therefore a man leaves his father and his mother and cleaves to his wife, and they become one flesh.

And the man and his wife were both naked, and were not ashamed.

Genesis 2:20–25

Since Charles Darwin's *The Origin of Species* first appeared in 1859, supporters of the theory of evolution and believers of the Biblical account of creation have disagreed. What is Darwin's theory and why do some people object to it so strongly? The following encyclopedia excerpt summarizes the theory and some of the objections raised against it.

Evolution

Carroll Lane Fenton

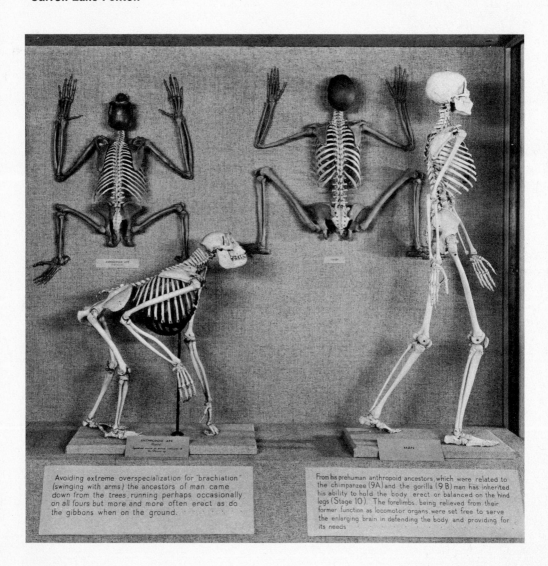

Avoiding extreme overspecialization for "brachiation" (swinging with arms) the ancestors of man came down from the trees, running perhaps occasionally on all fours but more and more often erect as do the gibbons when on the ground.

From his prehuman anthropoid ancestors, which were related to the chimpanzee (9A) and the gorilla (9 B) man has inherited his ability to hold the body erect or balanced on the hind legs (Stage 10). The forelimbs, being relieved from their former function as locomotor organs, were set free to serve the enlarging brain in defending the body and providing for its needs.

Darwin's Theory. Charles Darwin began with the fact that variations exist on such a scale that no two living things are exactly alike. He next showed that living things increased in number far more rapidly than people realized. In fact, living things reproduce in numbers so great that earth cannot provide room and food for all their abundant offspring. Members of each species therefore compete with each other for a chance to live, as well as with members of different species. In this competition any helpful variation gives its owner an advantage over neighbors that are not so well adapted. Individuals with such variations therefore will win the struggle for existence. They will live and reproduce, while forms not so well equipped will die.

Darwin called this process *natural selection,* or the "preservation of favored races in the struggle for life."

Objections to the Theory of Evolution. Many persons object to the theory of evolution because it conflicts with their religious beliefs. The religious objection to evolution stems from at least three convictions:

1. A conviction regarding the Bible. Many persons believe the account of Creation in the Book of Genesis to be a historical fact. Hence it is considered that God not only made the world by separate Almightly acts, but that He also created man, animals, and plants in such a way that they only would "yield fruit after their kind." Persons who hold this conviction usually do not believe in evolution from lower forms.

2. A conviction regarding God. In the Bible, God is held to be the Creator, the Sustainer, and the Ultimate End of all things. Many Christians believe that it is impossible to reconcile this conviction with the idea that evolutionary development has been brought about by natural forces present in organic life.

3. A conviction regarding the Gospel of the Christian religion. The reality of sin, and of redemption from sin, is held to be essential to the Christian faith. But if man is in the process of evolving from a lower state, sin tends to become mere imperfection, and the Gospel of redemption from the guilt of sin tends to lose all meaning.

Some persons also object to the theory of evolution on scientific grounds. Scientists themselves have disagreed on certain facts about evolution. The opponents of evolution say that in view of these disagreements the theory is far from being proved. It is denied that the facts of fossil arrangement, of comparative anatomy, of embryology, and so on, are evidence for the descent of species. Most scientists believe, for example, that the fact that the vertebrates all have many structures on the same plan proves that vertebrates all evolved from some common lower ancestor. But the opponents of the theory believe that this fact merely indicates that the Creator used the same pattern in making species of the same class.

The first paragraph of the article describes what Darwin called *natural selection.* Study it carefully and, from your own knowledge or observation of the animal world, write a paragraph detailing a real-life example of the process.

In some areas of the United States, opposition to Darwin's theory was so strong that laws were enacted prohibiting its being taught in the public schools. In Tennessee in 1925, John Scopes, a biology teacher, forced the issue to a crisis, deliberately violating the law by teaching the theory of evolution in his classroom. The "Scopes Monkey Trial," as it came to be called, attracted national attention because it focused on the issue of religion versus science. William Jennings Bryan, a famous politician who believed in a literal interpretation of the Bible, represented the state. Clarence Darrow, a legendary criminal defense lawyer, represented John Scopes.

In the historical dramatization of this trial, *Inherit the Wind,* Brady is Bryan, Drummond is Darrow, and Scopes is Cates. In the following scene, thirteen-year-old Howard, Cates' student, is being interrogated.

FROM Inherit the Wind

Jerome Lawrence and Robert E. Lee

Scene Two

The courtroom, two days later. It is bright midday, and the trial is in full swing. The JUDGE *is on the bench; the jury, lawyers, officials and spectators crowd the courtroom.* HOWARD, *the thirteen-year-old boy, is on the witness stand. He is wretched in a starched collar and Sunday suit. The weather is as relentlessly hot as before.* BRADY *is examining the boy, who is a witness for the prosecution.*

BRADY: Go on, Howard. Tell them what else Mr. Cates told you in the classroom.

HOWARD: Well, he said at first the earth was too hot for any life. Then it cooled off a mite, and cells and things begun to live.

BRADY: Cells?

HOWARD: Little bugs like, in the water. After that, the little bugs got to be bigger bugs, and sprouted legs and crawled up on the land.

BRADY: How long did this take, according to Mr. Cates?

HOWARD: Couple million years. Maybe longer. Then comes the fishes and the reptiles and the mammals. Man's a mammal.

BRADY: Along with the dogs and the cattle in the field: did he say that?

HOWARD: Yes, sir.

(DRUMMOND *is about to protest against prompting the witness; then he decides it isn't worth the trouble.*)

BRADY: Now, Howard, how did *man* come out of this slimy mess of bugs and serpents, according to your— "Professor"?

HOWARD: Man was sort of evoluted. From the "Old World Monkeys."

(BRADY *slaps his thigh.*)

BRADY: Did you hear that, my friends? "Old World Monkeys"! According to Mr. Cates, you and I aren't even descended from good American monkeys!

(*There is laughter.*) Howard, listen
carefully. In all this talk of bugs and
"*Evil-ution,*" of slime and ooze, did
Mr. Cates ever make any reference to
God?

HOWARD: Not as I remember.

BRADY: Or the miracle He achieved in
seven days as described in the beautiful
Book of Genesis?

HOWARD: No, sir.

(BRADY *stretches out his arms in an all-
embracing gesture.*)

BRADY: Ladies and gentlemen—

DRUMMOND: Objection! I ask that the
court remind the learned counsel that
this is not a Chautauqua tent. He is
supposed to be submitting evidence to
a jury. There are no ladies on the jury.

BRADY: Your Honor, I have no intention
of making a speech. There is no need.
I am sure that everyone on the jury,
everyone within the sound of this boy's
voice, is moved by his tragic confusion.
He has been taught that he wriggled up

Opposing Attorneys in Scopes Trial

Palm-leaf fan in hand, fundamentalist
William Jennings Bryan posed in the
steaming courtroom with agnostic
Clarence Darrow, the defense attorney.
At the beginning of the trial, Darrow
objected to an opening prayer offered
by the presiding judge, on the grounds
that any prayer at the moment was likely
to prejudice the jury against the
defendant. In the course of the trial
he summoned Bryan as a witness and
subjected him to a relentless
cross-examination that revealed Bryan's
lack of familiarity with modern science.

like an animal from the filth and the muck below! (*Continuing fervently, the spirit is upon him.*) I say that these Bible-haters, these "*Evil-utionists,*" are brewers of poison. And the legislature of this sovereign state has had the wisdom to demand that the peddlers of poison—in bottles or in books—clearly label the products they attempt to sell! (*There is applause.* HOWARD *gulps.* BRADY *points at the boy.*) I tell you, if this law is not upheld, this boy will become one of a generation shorn of its faith by the teachings of Godless science! But if the full penalty of the law is meted out to Bertram Cates, the faithful the whole world over, who are watching us here, and listening to our every word, will call this courtroom blessed! (*Applause. Dramatically,* BRADY *moves to his chair. Condescendingly, he waves to* DRUMMOND.)

BRADY: Your witness, sir.

(BRADY *sits.* DRUMMOND *rises, slouches toward the witness stand.*)

DRUMMOND: Well, I sure am glad Colonel Brady didn't make a speech! (*Nobody laughs. The courtroom seems to resent* DRUMMOND'S *gentle ridicule of the orator. To many, there is an effrontery in* DRUMMOND'S *very voice—folksy and relaxed. It's rather like a harmonica following a symphony concert.*) Howard, I heard you say that the world used to be pretty hot.

HOWARD: That's what Mr. Cates said.

DRUMMOND: You figure it was any hotter then than it is right now?

HOWARD: Guess it musta been. Mr. Cates read it to us from a book.

DRUMMOND: Do you know what book?

HOWARD: I guess that Mr. Darwin thought it up.

DRUMMOND: (*Leaning on the arm of the boy's chair*) You figure anything's wrong about that, Howard?

HOWARD: Well, I dunno—

DAVENPORT: (*Leaping up, crisply*) Objection, Your Honor. The defense is asking that a thirteen-year-old boy hand down an opinion on a question of morality!

DRUMMOND: (*To the* JUDGE) I am trying to establish, Your Honor, that Howard—or Colonel Brady—or Charles Darwin—or anyone in this courtroom—or *you,* sir—has the right to *think!*

JUDGE: Colonel Drummond, the right to think is not on trial here.

DRUMMOND: (*Energetically*) With all respect to the bench, I hold that the right to think is very much on trial! It is fearfully in danger in the proceedings of this court!

BRADY: (*Rises*) A *man* is on trial!

DRUMMOND: A thinking man! And he is threatened with fine and imprisonment because he chooses to speak what he thinks.

---

1. You are one of Howard's parents. Write a letter to Brady responding to his statement that "this boy will become one of a generation shorn of its faith by the teachings of a Godless science." Be sure to give your reasons for agreeing or disagreeing with the statement.

or

2. Reenact the phone conversation which took place between George Rapplyea, proprietor of a Dayton drugstore and Roger Baldwin, executive director of the American Civil Liberties Union. Mr. Rapplyea is calling to tell Mr. Baldwin that a local teacher, John Scopes, would like to accept the services of the Union to defend him when he goes to trial after deliberately violating the Tennessee law in order to test it. Mr. Baldwin has already publicly advertised that he will support anyone who is willing to test the case.

---

1. Fact, fiction, and opinion all appear in the selection from *Brave New World*. Find one example of each. In a small group, collect all your examples. After making sure that all of you agree they are valid, make a list of them on the blackboard to compare with the lists of the other groups.

2. For a debate, organize sides opposing and defending the Bokanovsky Process of producing human beings. In preparing their arguments, members of each side should consider the possible benefits and harmful effects of the process for individuals and for society as a whole.

Activities

3. A "pourquoi" tale is one which tells "how" something came to be the way it is. Rudyard Kipling wrote his *Just So Stories* to explain how the elephant got its trunk, the leopard its spots, the camel its hump, and so on. There are many American Indian tales about how the chipmunk got its stripes, the rabbit its cotton tail, etc. Referring to "Our First Man" and "What the Coyote Made" as models, write your own "pourquoi" tale.

4. Robert Ardrey wrote, "From the point of view of evolution, it is the specialized animal that must be regarded as the more advanced; the animal retaining his generality, the more primitive." Write a short essay explaining Ardrey's statement in terms of the encyclopedia selection on page 25. Use the paragraph about natural selection that you have written to help organize your ideas.

5. The Tennessee law under which John Scopes was prosecuted prohibited the teaching of any theory that denied the divine creation of mankind as it is revealed in the Bible. Assuming the role of a citizen of the town where the Scopes Trial is taking place, write a letter to the editor of the town newspaper, either supporting the Tennessee law or opposing it.

6. The Scopes Trial took place in Dayton, Tennessee, during July of 1925. With a group of classmates, research some of the more colorful events of the trial and design a one-page edition of the *Dayton Daily News* covering the trial. Include headlines and pictures with your articles and select some letters to the editor that were written for the preceding activity.

7. The Scopes Trial focused worldwide attention on the small town of Dayton. Trade and tourism increased over night. In *Inherit the Wind* the authors depict the atmosphere of the town as festive, complete with parades and picnics. Design a banner, bumper sticker, placard, poster, or lapel button for the occasion.

8. William Jennings Bryan and Clarence Darrow were colorful and controversial figures in American history. The Scopes Trial was the last public event of William Jennings Bryan's long public career—exhausted by the trial, he died a few days after it ended. Using the biographical sources in your school library, write the entry for one of these men as it might have appeared in the edition of *Who's Who* published the year after the Scopes trial. Follow the format of the current *Who's Who* entries in preparing your own entry. Do not exceed 250 words or write less than 150 words.

3
A Child
Is Born

Whatever our positions in life may be, no matter that our races, religions, or nationalities may differ, we all have at least one thing in common—the miracle of being born into the world. From that moment the daily events that help distinguish us as individuals begin to occur.

To get into the spirit of this chapter about birth, try to recapture the circumstances of your birthday by preparing a fact sheet. On it include your *full* name, the exact time and place of your birth, your size and weight at birth, and any other appropriate details (for example, weather conditions) that you can learn from your family or official records. Also, by checking in encyclopedia yearbooks or copies of old newspapers filed in your public library you can include a summary of the major historical events that happened on the day you were born.

Naked came I out of my mother's womb,
and naked shall I return thither.

Job 1:21

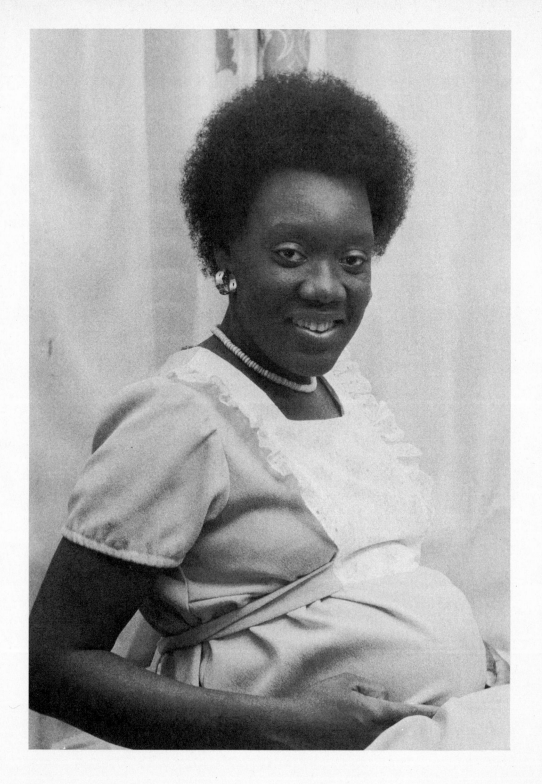

As a mother watches her child grow, she naturally wonders what her child will grow up to become. But what are a mother's feelings about her child as it is developing inside her body before birth? In the selection that follows, a mother-to-be marvels at the active, human life she feels inside her.

FROM If Beale Street Could Talk

James Baldwin

I cannot imagine what this thing inside of me is doing, but it appears to have acquired feet. Sometimes it is still, for days on end, sleeping perhaps, but more probably plotting—plotting its escape. Then, it turns, beating the water, churning, obviously becoming unspeakably bored in this element, and wanting out. We are beginning to have a somewhat acrid* dialogue, this thing and I—it kicks, and I smash an egg on the floor, it kicks, and suddenly the coffeepot is upside down on the table, it kicks, and the perfume on the back of my hand brings salt to the roof of my mouth, and my free hand weighs on the heavy glass counter, with enough force to crack it in two. . . . Be patient. I'm doing the best I can—and it kicks again, delighted to have elicited so furious a response. Please. Be still. And then, exhausted, or, as I suspect, merely cunning, it *is* still. . . . But it really *is* very cunning, it intends to live: it never moves while I am riding the subway, or when I am crossing a crowded street. But it grows heavier and heavier, its claims become more absolute with every hour. It is, in fact, staking its claim. The message is that it does not so much belong to *me*—though there is another, gentler kick, usually at night, signifying that it has no objection to belonging to me, that we may

even grow to be fond of each other—as *I* belong to *it*. . . .

I do not recognize my body at all, it is becoming absolutely misshapen. I try not to look at it, because I simply do not recognize it. Furthermore, I sometimes take something off in the evening, and have difficulty getting back into it in the morning. I can no longer wear high heels, they distort my sense of balance as profoundly as one's vision is distorted if one is blind in one eye. . . . It seems to me that I am gaining weight at the rate of about three hundred pounds an hour, and I do not dare speculate on what I will probably look like by the time this thing inside of me finally kicks itself out. . . . And yet, we are beginning to know each other, this thing, this creature, and I, and sometimes we are very, very friendly. It has something to say to me, and I must learn to listen—otherwise, I will not know what to say when it gets here.

What might a mother fantasize about the future of her unborn child? What hopes and fears may she have for her child? Using the same, first-person style of the selection, write down these thoughts and feelings that may run through a mother's mind as she prepares her breakfast.

* sarcastic

The time that a child is born is not always the most convenient for its mother. Television comedies make much use of taxicabs, subways, and elevators stuck between floors as the locales for inconvenient births. In a serious way, the last chapter of *The Grapes of Wrath,* John Steinbeck's novel about poor migrant farmers during the Depression of the 1930's, describes the birth of Rose of Sharon's baby in an old railroad boxcar. In the following excerpt, two curious children try to look on.

FROM The Grapes of Wrath

John Steinbeck

The two women pushed on the heavy sliding door, boosted it along until only a foot was open. "I'll git our lamp, too," Mrs. Wainwright said. Her face was purple with excitement. "Aggie," she called. "You take care of these here little fellas."

Ma nodded, "Tha's right. Ruthie! You an' Winfiel' go down with Aggie. Go on now."

"Why?" they demanded.

" 'Cause you got to. Rosasharn gonna have her baby."

"I wanta watch, Ma. Please let me."

"Ruthie! You git now. You git quick." There was no argument against such a tone. Ruthie and Winfield went reluctantly down the car. Ma lighted the lantern. Mrs. Wainwright brought her Rochester lamp down and set it on the floor, and its big circular flame lighted the boxcar brightly.

Ruthie and Winfield stood behind the brush pile and peered over. "Gonna have a baby, an' we're a-gonna see," Ruthie said softly. "Don't you make no noise now. Ma won't let us watch. If she looks this-a-way, you scrunch down behin' the brush. Then we'll see."

"There ain't many kids seen it," Winfield said.

"There ain't no kids seen it," Ruthie insisted proudly. "On'y us."

Down by the mattress, in the bright light of the lamp, Ma and Mrs. Wainwright held conference. Their voices were raised a little over the hollow beating of the rain. Mrs. Wainwright took a paring knife from her apron pocket and slipped it under the mattress. "Maybe it don't do no good," she said apologetically. "Our folks always done it. Don't do no harm, anyways."

Ma nodded. "We used a plow point. I guess anything sharp'll work, long as it can cut birth pains. I hope it ain't gonna be a long one."

"You feelin' awright now?"

Rose of Sharon nodded nervously. "Is it a-comin'?"

"Sure," Ma said. "Gonna have a nice baby. You jus' got to help us. Feel like you could get up an' walk?"

"I can try."

"That's a good girl," Mrs. Wainwright said. "That *is* a good girl. We'll he'p you, honey. We'll walk with ya." They helped her to her feet and pinned a blanket over her shoulders. Then Ma held her arm from one side, and Mrs. Wainwright from the other. They walked her to the brush pile and turned slowly and walked her back, over and over; and the rain drummed deeply on the roof.

Ruthie and Winfield watched anxiously. "When's she goin' to have it?" he demanded.

"Sh! Don't draw 'em. We won't be let to look."

Aggie joined them behind the brush pile. Aggie's lean face and yellow hair showed in the lamplight, and her nose was long and sharp in the shadow of her head on the wall.

Ruthie whispered, "You ever saw a baby bore?"

"Sure," said Aggie.

"Well, when's she gonna have it?"

"Oh, not for a long, long time."

"Well, how long?"

"Maybe not 'fore tomorrow mornin'."

"Shucks!" said Ruthie. "Ain't no good watchin' now, then.

Of all the billions of human births, not one has had such an impact on the course of Western civilization as the birth of Jesus Christ. No birthday is more widely celebrated each year. T. S. Eliot's poem, "Journey of the Magi," tells the story of the trip which the Three Wise Men made to see the newborn baby Jesus. The story is told as if one of the Magi were speaking many years after he witnessed that historical event.

Journey of the Magi

T. S. Eliot

'A COLD coming we had of it,
Just the worst time of the year
For a journey, and such a long journey:
The ways deep and the weather sharp,
The very dead of winter.'
And the camels galled[1], sore-footed, refractory[2],
Lying down in the melting snow.
There were times we regretted
The summer palaces on slopes, the terraces,
And the silken girls bringing sherbet.
Then the camel men cursing and grumbling
And running away, and wanting their liquor and women,
And the night-fires going out, and the lack of shelters,
And the cities hostile and the towns unfriendly
And the villages dirty and charging high prices:
A hard time we had of it.
At the end we preferred to travel all night,
Sleeping in snatches,
With the voices singing in our ears, saying
That this was all folly.

Then at dawn we came down to a temperate valley,
Wet, below the snow line, smelling of vegetation;
With a running stream and a water-mill beating the darkness,
And three trees on the low sky,
And an old white horse galloped away in the meadow.

[1] became sore from the rubbing of the saddles
[2] stubborn; hard to manage

Then we came to a tavern with vine-leaves over the lintel,
Six hands at an open door dicing for pieces of silver,
And feet kicking the empty wine-skins.
But there was no information, and so we continued
And arrived at evening, not a moment too soon
Finding the place; it was (you may say) satisfactory.

All this was a long time ago, I remember,
And I would do it again, but set down
This set down
This: were we led all that way for
Birth or Death? There was a Birth, certainly,
We had evidence and no doubt. I had seen birth and death,
But had thought they were different; this Birth was
Hard and Bitter agony for us, like Death, our death.
We returned to our places, these Kingdoms,
But no longer at ease here, in the old dispensation,
With an alien people clutching their gods.
I should be glad of another death.

Write an imaginary interview with the Wise Man who is the speaker of this poem. As the interviewer, your questions should be worded so that the Wise Man can identify *who* he is, *what* the purpose of his journey was, *where* he traveled, *when* he traveled, and *why* he feels the way he does about his journey. Try to base the Wise Man's answers, as much as possible, on information contained in the poem.

The Lamaze method of natural childbirth encourages the mother to prepare herself, by practicing and exercising beforehand, to deliver the baby without the need of anesthesia. The father is also encouraged to assist the mother as much as possible and to attend the birth. In *Thank You, Dr. Lamaze*, Marjorie Karmel describes the moments surrounding the birth of her baby boy.

FROM Thank You, Dr. Lamaze

Marjorie Karmel

This time it was very easy. I lay back, relaxed, and began to pant. But suddenly a sharp pain shot through my left leg. I winced and turned to Mme. Cohen. "Relax your leg," she said.

"I can't."

"You have a muscle cramp." She massaged it deftly, and in a few seconds it was gone. The minute my leg stopped hurting I became aware of a sensation that momentarily horrified me. Dr. Lamaze was working at turning down the baby's head, and I could feel everything he was doing! I had no sensation of pain at all, but I was shocked by the fact that my perception of what was happening was so complete. I felt the presence of the head, but I felt it the way I had felt the existence of a hole the dentist was drilling in my novocained tooth, touching it with my tongue. It seemed immense! Frighteningly so.

At that moment the delivery sequence of the movie flashed into my mind. I saw the doctor working the head down—just as Dr. Lamaze was doing at that minute. I knew there was nothing to be frightened of. I continued to pant, watching the delivery in my mind as it progressed.

"Forehead, eyes, nose . . ." I heard Dr. Lamaze call out slowly. "Come here, monsieur, come quickly! *Venez voir votre enfant naître!*—Come see your child is born!"

For an instant I thought of reminding Alex of his promise to stay at the head of the bed, but then I heard a tiny cry "La!" and realized how absurd I was. I felt something hot and wet on my leg. It was the baby's arm. Everyone shouted "Look!" Mme. Cohen helped me to raise my head and shoulders, and there I was looking into the face of my baby who was crying sweetly before he was completely born. A second more and Dr. Lamaze held him up for me to see. *"C'est un garçon, madame,"* he announced. He placed him on a sheet over my stomach so that I could hold him for a moment. It was incredible—he had my father's eyes, a Karmel forehead, and a cleft chin like Alex's, and yet he was obviously a real individual in his own right, from the very first moment. We named him immediately, Joseph Low, after my father. We even settled on the nickname "Pepi."

After we had admired him properly, Dr. Lamaze cut the cord and handed him to a nurse who took him off to the corner to be washed and dressed in the clothes that had been waiting for so long. It was twenty minutes past two, July the seventeenth, over twenty-four hours since I had felt the first contraction. I had forgotten all about the placenta, but Mme. Cohen reminded me to push when the contraction came, and I expelled it easily. Everyone examined it, including me; then all of them but Alex tidied up and went away. The baby, all dressed and wrapped in a blanket, French style, was in a little cradle beside my bed. Alex and I were alone with him. It was less than fifteen minutes after he had been born.

We sat and listened to the baby gurgle and hiccup in the quiet of the warm, still night. As it was so late, I was not going to be moved to my room until the morning. In spite of the tremendous exertion I had been through, I felt wonderfully exhilarated and excited. We talked quietly about the delivery and about our plans for the future, but mainly we were just happy to be there together with our newborn child. Finally Alex went off to send telegrams. I turned off the light, but for a long time I could not sleep. I lay in the dark and listened to the little noises my baby made and felt as happy as I had ever been.

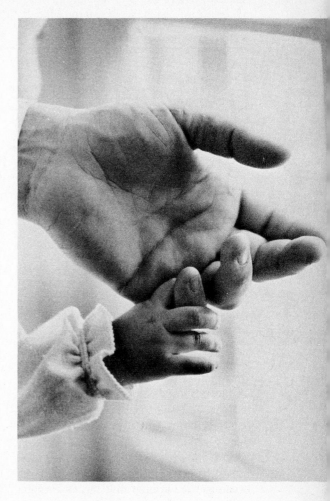

Bring in your own baby picture to mount with picture corners on a larger piece of paper for a bulletin board "baby gallery." When everyone's picture has been posted, the class can vote on the prettiest, funniest, etc. Class members may write appropriate captions for each picture on the paper (not on the picture), and guess who each baby is.

The veterinarian's task of helping in the births of livestock is more difficult in many ways than the task of the doctor who attends at human births, but the thrill and mystery of birth are much the same for both.

FROM All Creatures Great and Small

James Herriot

And in April, too, came the lambing. It came in a great tidal wave, the most vivid and interesting part of the veterinary surgeon's year, the zenith of the annual cycle, and it came as it always does when we were busiest with our other work. . . .

But in this first year I found a fascination in the work which has remained with me. Lambing, it seemed to me, had all the thrill and interest of calving without the hard labour. It was usually uncomfortable in that it was performed in the open; either in draughty pens improvised from straw bales and gates or more often out in the fields. It didn't seem to occur to the farmers that the ewe might prefer to produce her family in a warm place or that the vet may not enjoy kneeling for an hour in his shirt sleeves in the rain.

But the actual job was as easy as a song. After my experiences in correcting the malpresentations of calves it was delightful to manipulate these tiny creatures. Lambs are usually born in twos or threes and some wonderful mix-ups occur; tangles of heads and legs all trying to be first out and it is the vet's job to sort them around and decide which leg belonged to which head. I revelled in this. It was a pleasant change to be for once stronger and bigger than my patient, but I didn't overstress this advantage; I have not changed the opinion I formed then that there are just two things to remember in lambing—cleanliness and gentleness.

And the lambs. All young animals are appealing but the lamb has been given an unfair share of charm. The moments come back; of a bitterly cold evening when I had delivered twins on a wind-scoured hillside; the lambs shaking their heads convulsively and within minutes one of them struggling upright and making its way, unsteady, knock-kneed, towards the udder while the other followed resolutely on its knees.

The shepherd, his purpled, weather-roughened face almost hidden by the heavy coat which muffled him to his ears, gave a slow chuckle. "How . . . do they know?"

He had seen it happen thousands of times and he still wondered. So do I.

Although this excerpt focuses on lambing, the narrator makes several references to the difficulties of calving. Using no more than twenty-five words, write a precise statement explaining why the narrator prefers lambing to calving.

1. Carefully examine the Pennsylvania Dutch birth certificate on page 31. Design your own birth certificate after this model and include on it details from your fact sheet.

2. Gather as much information as you can find about the beliefs, folklore, and customs relating to childbirth. For example, Mrs. Wainwright in *The Grapes of Wrath* puts a paring knife under the mattress "to cut the birth pains." Attempt to gather information from people of different generations, cultures, or countries. Also look in books which deal with regional customs, such as *Foxfire II*. Try to determine whether each custom actually benefits childbearing or is merely superstition.

3. You are an artist who has been asked by a publisher to illustrate "Journey of the Magi" for a deluxe edition of T. S. Eliot's poems. You must submit in writing, for the publisher's approval, your ideas for three symbolic paintings, one for each stanza of the poem. Reread the poem and describe what each of your pictures will be like.

4. The births of many gods in mythology and of many great historical figures are surrounded by strange events. Find a story recounting the birth of a god or of a great person and write it up so that appropriate stories can be added to the class Myth Book. You may choose to consider the following names:

Athena   Alexander the Great
Dionysus   Jacob and Esau
Zeus   Julius Caesar
          Romulus and Remus

5. Assuming the role of the narrator of *All Creatures Great and Small*, write a few additional paragraphs to his tale to describe how his task at lambing and calving is similar to but more difficult than an obstetrician's task at the birth of a child.

Activities

6. Write an original story about the birth of an imaginary hero or public figure, such as a movie or sports star or a politician.

7. In a letter to your parents describe the neighborhood and the world in which you would want to raise your child. Use vivid details in your description.

8. Using the information you gathered on the fact sheet for your birthday, write a historical fiction story describing an incident that might have happened on the same day you were born. Tie the fact of your birth into the story.

Your children are not your children.
They are the sons and daughters of Life's longing for itself.
They come through you but not from you,
And though they are with you yet they belong not to you.
Kahlil Gibran

4 Milestones

The ceremonies and events that mark the passage from childhood to adulthood can be grouped into two categories: ceremonies and events that bring about a change in a person's social status, and those that merely celebrate a change which has taken place despite a ceremony. Birthday celebrations can fall into this second category: people grow older year by year whether or not they celebrate their birthdays. On the other hand, an eighteenth birthday marks a definite change in a person's social status: before the age of eighteen in the United States, a person cannot vote or enter into legal contracts, but after eighteen a person can assume these rights.

Begin your study of life's milestones by making a list of the major events and ceremonies marking your growth from childhood to adulthood. Include ceremonies and events that you anticipate to occur within the next several years. Consider also the milestones that are not the same for boys as for girls, and also those that are created and recognized only among children or adolescents. When your list is finished, decide whether a change in social status results from each milestone or whether that change would have taken place without a ceremony.

A milestone need not be a formal
ceremony or an event shared by every
other person. It can be, instead, a very
personal occasion, as when you realized
that you were becoming more of a person
for having experienced something. In
the life of Grandma Moses who lived to
be 101 there were many milestones. Only
in her seventies, when most people's
lives are beginning to end, did she
begin painting the pictures that made
her famous. In this selection from her
autobiography, she describes her first
job as a live-in maid at the age of twelve.

FROM My Life's History

Grandma Moses

1870,
now came the hard years,
Schooling was in those days in
the country three months in
summer three in winter,
little girls did not go to school
much in winter, owing to the
cold, and not warm enough
clothing, there for my school days
were limited,
altho I was Kept busy helping at
Home, and the neighbors,
when twelve years of age I left
Home to earn my own living as
then was called a hired girl,

This was a grand education
for me, in cooking, House
Keeping, in moralizeing and
mingleing with the out side world,

I went to live with a Family by
the name of mrs & mr Thomas
white sides, they were lovely
people, while well along in
years,

I was cared for by them as a
child of thair one,
Presbyterians by creed,
one of my duties was to drive the
Horse "old black joe" to church for
them on Sunday mornings, and
place boqwets on the Pulpit in
the church, and always remember the
text,
living with the whitesides
for three years, caring for
mrs whiteside who was an invalid
and died,

**Describe an important event in your own life, using
no more words than Grandma Moses did in this selection. Compare your present feelings about this event
with the feelings you had about it then.**

Keeping a diary or journal is one way to record the milestones of a life as they occur. In later years, the little events that helped form an entire personality can be relived. These diary entries of a high-school girl show that a family's move from one town to another can be as emotionally difficult as Grandma Moses' move to an entirely new family.

FROM Go Ask Alice

Anonymous

September 30

Wonderful news, Diary! We're moving. Daddy has been invited to become the Dean of Political Science at ————. Isn't that exciting! Maybe it will be like it was when I was younger. Maybe again he'll teach in Europe every summer and we'll go with him like we used to. Oh those were the fun, fun times! I'm going to start on a diet this very day. I will be a positively different person by the time we get to our new home. Not one more bite of chocolate or nary a french fried potato will pass my lips till I've lost ten globby pounds of lumpy lard. And I'm going to make a completely new wardrobe. Who cares about Ridiculous Roger? Confidentially, Diary, I still care. I guess I'll always love him, but maybe just before we leave and I'm thin and my skin is absolutely flawless and petal smooth and clear, and I have clothes like a fashion model he'll ask me for another date.

January 1

Last night I went to a New Year's party at Scott's house. The kids got a little wild. Some of the boys were juicing it up. I came home early saying I didn't feel well, but actually it's just that I'm so excited about moving in two days that I am beside myself.

Frankly, I wouldn't dare say this to anybody but you, Diary, but I'm not too sure I'm going to make it in a new town. I barely made it in our old town where I knew everybody and they knew me. I've never even allowed myself to think about it before, but I really haven't much to offer in a new situation. Oh dear God, help me adjust, help me be accepted, help me belong, don't let me be a social outcast and a drag on my family. Here I go bawling again, what a boob, but there isn't any more I can do about that than there is I can do about moving. So you're wet again! It's a good thing diaries don't catch cold!

January 4

We're here! It's barely January 4, only ten minutes after one, and Tim and Alex have been quarreling and Mom has either the stomach flu or she's just upset because of the excitement; anyway Dad has had to stop twice so that she could throw up. Something went wrong and the lights haven't been turned on and I think even Dad is about ready to turn around and go back home. Mom had made a diagram of where she wanted the movers to put everything and they got it all fouled up. So we're all just going to roll up in bedding and sleep in whichever bed is handy.

I'm glad I've got my little pocket flashlight, at least I can see to write. Confidentially the house looks pretty weird and haunted, but maybe that's because there are no curtains up or anything. Maybe things will look brighter tomorrow. They certainly couldn't look worse.

January 6

Sorry I haven't had time to write for two days, but we haven't stopped. We're still trying to get curtains hung and boxes unpacked and things put away. The house is beautiful. The walls are thick dark wood and there are two steps going down to a long sunken living room. I've apologized to every room about the way I felt last night.

I'm still worried about school and TODAY I must go. I wish Tim were in high school. Even a little brother would be better than no one, but he is in his second year of junior high. Already he's met a boy down the street his own age and I should be happy for him, but I'm not—I'm sad for myself. Alexandria is still in grade school and one of the professors lives close and has a daughter her age, so she will go directly to his home after school. How lucky can you get, built-in friends and everything? For me, as usual, nothing! A big fat nothing, and probably just what I deserve. I wonder if the kids wear the same things they do at home? Oh, I hope I'm not so different they'll all stare at me. Oh, how I wish I had a friend! But I better paste on the big phony smile, Mother is calling and I must respond with an "attitude that will determine my altitude."

One, two, three, and here goes the martyr.

Evening, January 6

Oh Diary it was miserable! It was the loneliest, coldest place in the world. Not one single person spoke to me during the whole endlessly long day. During lunch period I fled to the nurse's office and said I had a headache. Then I cut my last class and went by the drugstore and had a chocolate malt, a double order of french fried potatoes and a giant Hershey Bar. There had to be something in life that was worthwhile. All the time I ate, I hated myself for being childish. Hurt as I am when I think about it I have probably done the same thing to every new person that came to my schools, either ignored them completely or stared at them out of curiosity. So, I'm just getting "cut" back and I guess I deserve it, but oh, am I ever suffering! I ache even in my fingernails and toenails and in my hair follicles.

March 18

Well, I've finally found a friend at school. She's as cloddy and misfitting as I am. But I guess that old poke about birds of a feather is true. One night Gerta came to pick me up for the movies and my folks were everything but rude to her. Imagine my long-suffering, sweet-mouthed mother being tempted to utter a slimy phrase about my drab-looking nobody friend. I wonder why she doesn't take a second look at her drab-looking nobody daughter, or would that be too much for the well-groomed, thin, charming wife of the great Professor, who might be the President of the school within a few years.

I could see them all squirming a little even as I have been squirming ever since we got to this impregnable hole.

Write a letter to Alice telling her what to expect if it were your neighborhood and your school that she had moved to. Warn her about things that she should be careful of and advise her on how to become accepted by your friends.

Among some primitive tribes, young people must undergo tests of bravery or endurance before they can be considered adult members of the community. In our own culture, fairy tales often present similar situations in which a young hero or heroine performs great and dangerous feats. According to David Leeming in *Mythology: The Voyage of the Hero,* there is more significance to these tales than mere heroic adventure:

In the myth the child proves himself by confronting a physical force or by receiving a divine blessing. He kills the giant—the irrational authority of the adult who would suppress him. He kills the monster or wild animal— the monstrous and wild desires and instincts within us all. He draws the sword from the rock, proving that he is equal to his father, who put it there.

A fairy tale, then, can be symbolic of a significant milestone on the road to adulthood.

Jack and the Beanstalk

But Jack jumped down and got hold of the axe and gave a chop at the beanstalk which cut it half in two. The ogre felt the beanstalk shake and quiver so he stopped to see what was the matter. Then Jack gave another chop with the axe, and the beanstalk was cut in two and began to topple over. Then the ogre fell down and broke his crown, and the beanstalk came toppling after.

The Red Ettin

There was once a widow that lived on a small bit of ground, which she rented from a farmer. And she had two sons; and by-and-by it was time for the wife to send them away to seek their fortune. So. . . .

Complete the fairy tale of "The Red Ettin" so that it will follow a traditional fairy-tale plot. Use suitable language, settings, and characters to make your fairy tale authentic.

The legendary life of King Arthur reads
almost like a fairy tale. It is filled with
adventure and brave deeds. Probably
no milestone in the life of the King was
as important as the moment when young
Arthur proved himself worthy of kingship
before the commoners and nobles of
England.

The Coronation of Arthur

Sir Thomas Malory

(*adapted into Modern English by Keith Baines*)

During the years that followed the death
of King Uther, while Arthur was still a
child, the ambitious barons fought one
another for the throne, and the whole of
Britain stood in jeopardy. Finally the day
came when the Archbishop of Canterbury, on the advice of Merlin, summoned
the nobility to London for Christmas
morning. In his message the Archbishop
promised that the true succession to the
British throne would be miraculously revealed. Many of the nobles purified themselves during their journey, in the hope that
it would be to them that the succession
would fall.

The Archbishop held his service in the
city's greatest church (St. Paul's), and
when matins[1] were done the congregation
filed out to the yard. They were con-
fronted by a marble block into which had
been thrust a beautiful sword. The block
was four feet square, and the sword
passed through a steel anvil which had
been struck in the stone, and which projected a foot from it. The anvil had been
inscribed with letters of gold:

WHOSO PULLETH OUTE THIS SWERD OF
THIS STONE AND ANVYLD IS RIGHTWYS
KYNGE BORNE OF ALL BRYTAYGNE[2]

The congregation was awed by this
miraculous sight, but the Archbishop for-
bade anyone to touch the sword before
mass had been heard. After mass, many
of the nobles tried to pull the sword out
of the stone, but none was able to, so a
watch of ten knights was set over the
sword, and a tournament proclaimed for

[1] a church service sung at morning

[2] Britain

49

New Year's Day, to provide men of noble blood with the opportunity of proving their right to the succession.

Sir Ector, who had been living on an estate near London, rode to the tournament with Arthur and his own son Sir Kay, who had been recently knighted. When they arrived at the tournament, Sir Kay found to his annoyance that his sword was missing from its sheath, so he begged Arthur to ride back and fetch it from their lodging.

Arthur found the door of the lodging locked and bolted, the landlord and his wife having left for the tournament. In order not to disappoint his brother, he rode on to St. Paul's, determined to get for him the sword which was lodged in the stone. The yard was empty, the guard also having slipped off to see the tournament, so Arthur strode up to the sword, and, without troubling to read the inscription, tugged it free. He then rode straight back to Sir Kay and presented him with it.

Sir Kay recognized the sword, and taking it to Sir Ector, said "Father, the succession falls to me, for I have here the sword that was lodged in the stone." But Sir Ector insisted that they should all ride to the churchyard, and once there bound Sir Kay by oath to tell how he had come by the sword. Sir Kay then admitted that Arthur had given it to him. Sir Ector turned to Arthur and said, "Was the sword not guarded?"

"It was not," Arthur replied.

"Would you please thrust it into the stone again?" said Sir Ector. Arthur did so, and first Sir Ector and then Sir Kay tried to remove it, but both were unable to. Then Arthur, for the second time, pulled it out. Sir Ector and Sir Kay both knelt before him.

"Why," said Arthur, "do you both kneel before me?"

"My lord," Sir Ector replied, "there is only one man living who can draw the sword from the stone, and he is the true-born King of Britain." Sir Ector then told Arthur the story of his birth and upbringing.

"My dear father," said Arthur, "for so I shall always think of you—if, as you say, I am to be king, please know that any request you have to make is already granted."

Sir Ector asked that Sir Kay should be made Royal Seneschal[3], and Arthur declared that while they both lived it should be so. Then the three of them visited the Archbishop and told him what had taken place.

All those dukes and barons with ambitions to rule were present at the tournament on New Year's Day. But when all of them had failed, and Arthur alone had succeeded in drawing the sword from the stone, they protested against one so young, and of ignoble[4] blood, succeeding to the throne.

The secret of Arthur's birth was known only to a few of the nobles surviving from the days of King Uther. The Archbishop urged them to make Arthur's cause their own; but their support proved ineffective. The tournament was repeated at Candlemas[5] and at Easter, and with the same outcome as before.

Finally at Pentecost[6], when once more Arthur alone had been able to remove the sword, the commoners arose with a tumul-

[3] a person in charge of a royal household
[4] not noble; common
[5] a church feast celebrated February 2
[6] a church feast celebrated on the seventh Sunday after Easter

tuous cry and demanded that Arthur should at once be made king. The nobles, knowing in their hearts that the commoners were right, all knelt before Arthur and begged forgiveness for having delayed his succession for so long. Arthur forgave them, and then, offering his sword at the high altar, was dubbed first knight of the realm. The coronation took place a few days later, when Arthur swore to rule justly, and the nobles swore him their allegiance.

In the legend of King Arthur, the boy had to perform an important task to achieve manhood. Rewrite the Arthurian legend in twentieth-century terms, substituting a modern symbol of adulthood for the act of pulling the sword from the anvil and stone. Be sure the circumstances and setting of your tale reflect twentieth-century life.

Do you remember the first time you bought yourself an outfit that made you feel really special? For many people that first assertion of individuality through clothing is a memorable milestone. For Malcolm X growing up during the 1940's, the sign of the "hip" young man was the zoot suit.

FROM The Autobiography of Malcolm X

One of these nights, I remarked that I had saved about half enough to get a zoot.

"Save?" Shorty couldn't believe it. "Homeboy, you never heard of credit?" He told me he'd call a neighborhood clothing store the first thing in the morning, and that I should be there early.

A salesman, a young Jew, met me when I came in. "You're Shorty's friend?" I said I was; it amazed me—all of Shorty's contacts. The salesman wrote my name on a form, and the Roseland as where I worked, and Ella's address as where I lived. Shorty's name was put down as recommending me. The salesman said, "Shorty's one of our best customers."

I was measured, and the young salesman picked off a rack a zoot suit that was just wild: sky-blue pants thirty inches in the knee and angle-narrowed down to twelve inches at the bottom, and a long coat that pinched my waist and flared out below my knees.

As a gift, the salesman said, the store would give me a narrow leather belt with my initial "L" on it. Then he said I ought to also buy a hat, and I did—blue, with a feather in the four-inch brim. Then the store gave me another present: a long, thick-linked, gold-plated chain that swung down lower than my coat hem. I was sold forever on credit.

When I modeled the zoot for Ella, she took a long look and said, "Well, I guess it had to happen." I took three of those twenty-five-cent sepia-toned, while-you-wait pictures of myself, posed the way "hipsters" wearing their zoots would "cool it"—hat dangled, knees drawn close together, feet wide apart, both index fingers jabbed toward the floor. The long coat and swinging chain and the Punjab pants were much more dramatic if you stood that way. One picture, I autographed and airmailed to my brothers and sisters in Lansing, to let them see how well I was doing. I gave another one to Ella, and the third to Shorty, who was really moved: I could tell by the way he said, "Thanks, homeboy." It was part of our "hip" code not to show that kind of affection.

Write a dialogue about an important experience involving clothing. In writing your dialogue, choose characters with opposing points of view, such as parent and child, salesperson and customer, employer and employee.

Because of the seriousness of the responsibilities involved, marriage is probably the greatest milestone celebrated by society. Because of our religious and cultural traditions, each of us has a definite idea of what a marriage ceremony should be like, but imagine yourself getting married in a centuries-old Laotian ceremony lasting two weeks!

How a Denver Man Bought a Bride

Olga Curtis

John M. Gilliland of Denver knows exactly what his wife is worth: 300 grams of 24-karat gold, $400 cash and two bowls of betel nut.

That was the "bride-price" for Jenny, the Lao-Chinese girl he married last November. It came to about $1,100 altogether—double the going rate for a bride in Laos—but Gilliland considers it small payment for the happy ending to his unusual love story. He believes he is the first Caucasian ever to marry a Lao-Chinese girl in traditional Lao rites. . . .

By tradition, Jenny was meant to stay home until her mother could arrange a suitable marriage for her, at about age 17. She explains:

"Lao girls marry very young, to whatever man the mother chooses. There is no dating in Laos. Young people can go out only in groups.

"If a girl reaches 20 without marrying, it is a great loss of face for her family. It means the mother could not make a suitable arrangement, or that no one would pay the bride-price. And to marry without the consent of both mothers would be disrespectful." . . .

On Oct. 5, 1972, John and Jenny were married in a civil ceremony at the American Embassy.

After that ceremony, John delivered his bride back into her mother's custody. He says with a grin:

"We were legally married but we could not live together because we hadn't been married according to Lao custom. I still had to ask Jenny's mother for permission every time I took Jenny out and I had to bring her back to her mother every night."

The traditional wedding a month later lasted two weeks. It began on Nov. 8 with a formal engagement agreed upon by the older women. For the next 12 days, both John and Jenny and their families were busy hand-delivering wedding invitations and personally inviting relatives to the wedding celebration. Jenny bought a wedding dress of silk shot with gold. John had to buy the "bride-price" gold, in the form of two heavy coiled bracelets, and arrange for his wedding costume—a sarong of four yards of blue silk, and a white silk jacket. The Sananikone family lent him $1,000 worth of gold chains and buttons to decorate the jacket properly. John also had to meet his real parents who flew in from Denver via Bangkok, and find a Lao costume for his mother.

Meanwhile the women of Jenny's family were busy decorating her home and cooking food for 200 guests.

Finally, on the morning of Nov. 21, the wedding celebration began.

It is a Lao tradition for the groom's family to pretend to fight for the bride. So, to the delight of a crowd of Lao citizens and all of John's co-workers at the Dooley Foundation, red-haired John in his blue sarong marched on Jenny's house. The bridegroom, glittering with gold and carrying two candles wrapped in flowers, was flanked by his Lao "brother," Jim Sananikone, on one side and his best man, Chantawong Sagnasith, on the other. Sagnasith carried a red umbrella, the symbol of "respectful protection," over John's head.

When they got to Jenny's house, they yelled to be let in. John recalls the dialogue went something like this:

"Let me in!"

"Why?"

"To get my bride."

"How much will you pay?"

"Twenty Baht of gold."

"Not enough! You can't pass."

This sham opposition ended abruptly when John slipped red envelopes of money under the gate. After that Jenny's family did most of the yelling: "He's come to get his bride!"

Meantime, Jenny had made her appearance in the room where 200 barefoot guests waited. The Maw Phon, or Lao "doctor of blessings," an old man who would sing the traditional wedding chants, waited with Jenny's family and John's two families in the center of the room, squatting on a special bridal carpet provided by her grandmother. Jenny bowed low to her mother, and on her knees asked for forgiveness of any daughterly sins and for permission to marry. Her mother formally gave permission, and the Maw Phon told Jenny to sit and wait for her husband.

John was preceded into the room by a procession of women from his families, carrying six silver bowls. The bowls contained the gold bracelets, the cash and the traditional betel nut payment. After they were placed on the carpet next to Jenny's two bridal candles surrounded by marigold and clover blossoms on bamboo sticks, the groom entered.

John lit Jenny's candles with his two candles, placing all four together. Then he squatted in front of the candles in "respectful ceremony" position, left foot into the crook of his right knee, hands held out with palms together in prayer attitude. Jenny took her place at his left, squatting with her right foot into her left knee, her hands also in prayer position.

Her mother then declared that the marriage might begin. The Maw Phon chanted for 20 minutes ("The gist of all that was that Jenny and I were together for life," says John) and finally offered blessings that "flowed" to the bridal couple along long white cotton strings stretched through the flowers and candles.

Afterwards, John and Jenny formally asked her mother, his Lao family and his real parents for blessings, which were given by tying short white cotton strings around their wrists.

It was only when the guests started feasting on dried meat, chicken, noodles, rice and meat balls that John learned his new mother-in-law had really accepted him.

After making sure no one was watching, Mrs. Luangphinith slipped him an envelope under the table. "For travel," she said with a smile.

The envelope contained the $400 cash he had paid for Jenny.

Write a description of your ideal wedding ceremony. Include as many details about the ceremony as you can.

---

1. When Grandma Moses was twelve, the custom of apprenticing or "hiring out" was a common way of educating and caring for the children of poor families. Suppose, because of hard times, this custom were revived. Write several diary entries which you might write if you had left home and been placed with a family in another community who required your services.

2. (a) Notice the dates of the entries in Alice's diary between the time she begins school and the time she finally finds a friend. Friendship is important for her sense of well-being and for her need to belong. In your own life, you may wish that you had more or better friends. Write up a want ad for a best friend. Include all the characteristics of your ideal friend that would suit your own personality and interests. Do not sign your name to the ad.

(b) Collect all the want ads from the class and redistribute them at random so that each student does not know who wrote the ad that is received. Write a statement why you would or would not want to respond to that particular want ad.

Activities

3. Using the resources in your school library, research some of the ceremonies or tests of endurance that young people of primitive tribes must undergo before they are accepted as adult members of the community. Try to determine the reasons why these ceremonies and tests are believed to be necessary.

4. Many fairy tales deal with the theme of the hero's proving himself and finding some reward. Read one of the following tales and make a short oral report to the class about how your story dealt with passing a test and acquiring some mark of success as a result: "Aladdin," "The Gallant Tailor," "Dick Whittington and His Cat," "The Bottled Spirit," "The Wise Griffon," "Jack and the Beanstalk," "Puss in Boots," "The Three Little Pigs," "The Lad Who Went to the North Wind."

5. Clothes and hair styles have always been symbols of social status and people's images of themselves. Look through magazines and collect pictures which illustrate as many different styles as possible. Working with some classmates, make a large mural by mounting your pictures under headings of different social groups.

6. (a) As a believer in the feminist movement, you are offended by the Laotian practice of purchasing a wife as if she were a piece of merchandise. Write a letter to the editor of the *Denver Post* protesting this custom and a Denver man's participation in it.

or

(b) Since many Americans regard the practice of arranged marriages as terrible, write a defense of the custom to the editor of the *Denver Post* in which you show how it can benefit both the husband and wife and their families.

7. Collect advertisements and greeting cards dealing with the milestones in a person's life. Display them on the bulletin board chronologically.

5

Facing Death

The subject of death upsets many people;
nevertheless, it is an event that everyone must
face. Unlike our births, which were all much the
same, the ways of dying are many. When we
are young and dream about the possibilities
that the future holds, it is natural to think
about the ways in which we may die.

Write a short account of your own death as you
imagine it may be. Will your death be heroic
or average? At home or in a hospital, or in some
distant place? Will it be accidental or natural?
Will you be old or still young? Who will be with
you? When you have finished your imaginary
account, discuss what you have written with a
group of classmates and try to determine why
each person imagined that particular way of
dying. Finally, with the entire class, conduct a
survey to determine each student's attitude
toward death. Record the results on the
blackboard.

The Vision of Death

And I looked, and behold a pale horse:
and his name that sat on him was Death

Revelation 6: 8

Robert Frost took the title for the
following poem from a line in
Shakespeare's *Macbeth*. When Macbeth
is told of the death of his wife he says,
"...all our yesterdays have lighted fools
the way to dusty death. Out, out, brief
candle!" In this poem about a Vermont
farm boy cutting firewood with a buzz
saw, Frost wants us to think how
quickly death can extinguish life, like a
puff of breath putting out a candle.

"Out, Out—"

Robert Frost

The buzz saw snarled and rattled in the yard
And made dust and dropped stove-length sticks of wood,
Sweet-scented stuff when the breeze drew across it.
And from there those lifted eyes could count
Five mountain ranges one behind the other
Under the sunset far into Vermont.
And the saw snarled and rattled, snarled and rattled.
As it ran light, or had to bear a load.
And nothing happened: day was all but done.
Call it a day, I wish they might have said
To please the boy by giving him the half hour
That a boy counts so much when saved from work.
His sister stood beside them in her apron
To tell them "Supper." At the word, the saw,
As if to prove saws knew what supper meant,
Leaped out at the boy's hand, or seemed to leap—
He must have given the hand. However it was,
Neither refused the meeting. But the hand!
The boy's first outcry was a rueful laugh,
As he swung toward them holding up the hand,
Half in appeal, but half as if to keep
The life from spilling. Then the boy saw all—
Since he was old enough to know, big boy

"... for it might end, you know," said Alice to herself, "in my going out altogether, like a candle. I wonder what I should be like then?" And she tried to fancy what the flame of a candle looks like after the candle is blown out. . . .

Lewis Carroll,
Alice's Adventures in Wonderland

Doing a man's work, though a child at heart—
He saw all spoiled. "Don't let him cut my hand off—
The doctor, when he comes. Don't let him, sister!"
So. But the hand was gone already.
The doctor put him in the dark of ether.
He lay and puffed his lips out with his breath.
And then—the watcher at his pulse took fright.
No one believed. They listened at his heart.
Little—less—nothing!—and that ended it.
No more to build on there. And they, since they
Were not the one dead, turned to their affairs.

The tone of the poem is very unemotional and matter-of-fact in its description of the boy's death. The last lines of the poem indicate how unconcerned and detached the doctors were once the boy died. It seems that the poem says that the boy's life signifies nothing. Imagine that the dead boy lived in the same town with you and that this poem appeared in your local newspaper shortly after his death. Write a letter to the newspaper either praising or criticizing the poem's attitude toward the boy's death.

For the boy in Frost's poem, death
was sudden and unexpected. But how
do people face death as they grow
older day by day? In this excerpt from
a poem by Randall Jarrell, a middle-aged
woman is thinking about her life and
death as she drives home from the
supermarket.

FROM Next Day

Randall Jarrell

I am afraid, this morning, of my face.
It looks at me
From the rear-view mirror, with the eyes I hate,
The smile I hate. It's plain, lined look
Of gray discovery
Repeats to me: "You're old." That's all, I'm old.

And yet I'm afraid, as I was at the funeral
I went to yesterday.
My friend's cold made-up face, granite among its flowers,
Her undressed, operated-on, dressed body
Were my face and body.
As I think of her I hear her telling me

How young I seem; I *am* exceptional;
I think of all I have.
But really no one is exceptional,
No one has anything, I'm anybody,
I stand beside my grave
Confused with my life, that is commonplace and solitary.

**Imagine that the woman who is the
speaker of this poem is a friend
of yours and has confided her fear
of death to you. Write a response
to her that you feel would comfort
her.**

Thinking about death brought fear to
the woman of "Next Day." Does the
fear ever disappear? In the following
excerpt from a Russian story, the main
character finds that joy replaces his
fear as death approaches.

FROM The Death of Ivan Ilych

Leo Tolstoy

And suddenly it grew clear to him that what had been oppressing him and would
not leave him was all dropping away at once from two sides, from ten sides,
and from all sides. He was sorry for them, he must act so as not to hurt them:
release them and free himself from these sufferings. "How good and how simple!"
he thought. "And the pain?" he asked himself. "What has become of it?
Where are you, pain?"

He turned his attention to it.

"Yes, here it is. Well, what of it? Let the pain be."

"And death . . . where is it?"

He sought his former accustomed fear of death and did not find it.
"Where is it? What death?" There was no fear because there was no death.

In place of death there was light.

"So that's what it is!" he suddenly exclaimed aloud. "What joy!"

To him all this happened in a single instant, and the meaning of that instant
did not change. For those present his agony continued for another two hours.
Something rattled in his throat, his emaciated body twitched, then the gasping and
rattle became less and less frequent.

"It is finished!" said someone near him.

He heard these words and repeated them in his soul.

"Death is finished," he said to himself. "It is no more!"

He drew in a breath, stopped in the midst of a sigh, stretched out, and died.

Write a short sequel to the story, in which the dying man, imagining that the figure of Death has entered his room, tells why he
welcomes his coming rather than dreads it.

The preceding selections have
concentrated more or less on the feelings
of the person who is dying. But like the
unemotional speaker and detached
doctors in "Out, Out—," David in this
selection is a witness to the death of
another person—his father. David
wants to discuss a past quarrel which
led to his leaving home, but he discovers
that this event, so important to him,
is now meaningless to his father.

FROM Run Softly, Go Fast

Barbara Werbsa

I did not recognize the person in the bed.
He was too small to be my father, too
thin. He looked like no one I had ever
seen before. A tube in his arm, a plastic
bottle overhead. His eyes were closed.
Then I saw Mom sitting in the corner,
and a nurse standing by the window . . .
and realized that I was in the right room.

"Mom . . . how is he?"

Her face was blank as she glanced at
me. "He had a bad night. He's resting."

"Oh. I'm sorry."

"Mrs. Williams—this is my son,
David."

The nurse smiled at me, but I couldn't
smile back. "He looks pretty bad."

"That's because you haven't seen him
since spring." Mom's voice was cold, and
the nurse must have noticed it because
she said she wanted to step outside for a
moment. "Do that, Mrs. Williams. You
must be tired."

Then we were alone, not meeting each
other's eyes. "I'm sorry I didn't come before," I said. "I've been sort of busy."

"You don't have to make excuses."

"How is he—really?"

"They have him on morphine."

"A lot of pain?"

"Yes, but he's very good about it. . . ."

Dad opened his eyes and mumbled
something. "What, Leo? I didn't hear
you." She walked over to him.

"I asked you what time it was."

"One-thirty."

"Is it time for my shot?"

"Not for a little while."

"I thought it was time."

"Is the pain very bad?"

"No, no, but I had a strange dream
. . . a big boat."

"Leo, Davy's here."

"Really?"

I went to the bed and took his hand.

...eceding selections have
...ntrated more or less on the feelings
...person who is dying. But like the
...tional speaker and detached
...rs in "Out, Out—," David in this
...ion is a witness to the death of
...r person—his father. David
...to discuss a past quarrel which
...his leaving home, but he discovers
...is event, so important to him,
... meaningless to his father.

Run Softly, Go Fast

...ra Werbsa

...not recognize the person in the bed.
...as too small to be my father, too
...He looked like no one I had ever
...before. A tube in his arm, a plastic
...overhead. His eyes were closed.
...I saw Mom sitting in the corner,
...nurse standing by the window . . .
...ealized that I was in the right room.
...Mom . . . how is he?"

...er face was blank as she glanced at
...He had a bad night. He's resting."

...Oh. I'm sorry."

...Mrs. Williams—this is my son,
...d."

...he nurse smiled at me, but I couldn't
...back. "He looks pretty bad."

...That's because you haven't seen him
...spring." Mom's voice was cold, and
...urse must have noticed it because
...aid she wanted to step outside for a
...ent. "Do that, Mrs. Williams. You
...be tired."

Then we were alone, not meeting each
other's eyes. "I'm sorry I didn't come before," I said. "I've been sort of busy."

"You don't have to make excuses."

"How is he—really?"

"They have him on morphine."

"A lot of pain?"

"Yes, but he's very good about it. . . ."

Dad opened his eyes and mumbled
something. "What, Leo? I didn't hear
you." She walked over to him.

"I asked you what time it was."

"One-thirty."

"Is it time for my shot?"

"Not for a little while."

"I thought it was time."

"Is the pain very bad?"

"No, no, but I had a strange dream
. . . a big boat."

"Leo, Davy's here."

"Really?"

I went to the bed and took his hand.

Doing a man's work, though a child at heart—
He saw all spoiled. "Don't let him cut my hand off—
The doctor, when he comes. Don't let him, sister!"
So. But the hand was gone already.
The doctor put him in the dark of ether.
He lay and puffed his lips out with his breath.
And then—the watcher at his pulse took fright.
No one believed. They listened at his heart.
Little—less—nothing!—and that ended it.
No more to build on there. And they, since they
Were not the one dead, turned to their affairs.

The tone of the poem is very unemotional and matter-of-fact in its description of the boy's death. The last lines of the poem indicate how unconcerned and detached the doctors were once the boy died. It seems that the poem says that the boy's life signifies nothing. Imagine that the dead boy lived in the same town with you and that this poem appeared in your local newspaper shortly after his death. Write a letter to the newspaper either praising or criticizing the poem's attitude toward the boy's death.

For the boy in Frost's poem, death was sudden and unexpected. But how do people face death as they grow older day by day? In this excerpt from a poem by Randall Jarrell, a middle-aged woman is thinking about her life and death as she drives home from the supermarket.

FROM Next Day

Randall Jarrell

I am afraid, this morning, of my face.
It looks at me
From the rear-view mirror, with the eyes I hate,
The smile I hate. It's plain, lined look
Of gray discovery
Repeats to me: "You're old." That's all, I'm old.

And yet I'm afraid, as I was at the funeral
I went to yesterday.
My friend's cold made-up face, granite among its flowers,
Her undressed, operated-on, dressed body
Were my face and body.
As I think of her I hear her telling me

How young I seem; I *am* exceptional;
I think of all I have.
But really no one is exceptional,
No one has anything, I'm anybody,
I stand beside my grave
Confused with my life, that is commonplace and solitary.

Imagine that the woman who is the speaker of this poem is a friend of yours and has confided her fear of death to you. Write a response to her that you feel would comfort her.

Thinking about death brought fear to the woman of "Next Day." Does the fear ever disappear? In the following excerpt from a Russian story, the main character finds that joy replaces his fear as death approaches.

FROM The Death of Ivan

Leo Tolstoy

And suddenly it grew clear to him that what had been oppre[ssing him and would] not leave him was all dropping away at once from two sides, [from ten sides,] and from all sides. He was sorry for them, he must act so as [to] release them and free himself from these sufferings. "How go[od and how simple!"] he thought. "And the pain?" he asked himself. "What has be[come of it?] Where are you, pain?"

He turned his attention to it.

"Yes, here it is. Well, what of it? Let the pain be."

"And death . . . where is it?"

He sought his former accustomed fear of death and did n[ot find it.] "Where is it? What death?" There was no fear because there [was no death.]

In place of death there was light.

"So that's what it is!" he suddenly exclaimed aloud. "Wha[t joy!"]

To him all this happened in a single instant, and the mea[ning of that instant] did not change. For those present his agony continued for an[other two hours.] Something rattled in his throat, his emaciated body twitched, [then the] rattle became less and less frequent.

"It is finished!" said someone near him.

He heard these words and repeated them in his soul.

"Death is finished," he said to himself. "It is no more!"

He drew in a breath, stopped in the midst of a sigh, stretc[hed out . . .]

Write a short sequel to the story, in which the dyi[ng man, imag-] ining that the figure of Death has entered his room, [. . .] welcomes his coming rather than dreads it.

Goodbye my friend, it's hard to die
When all the birds are singing in the sky
Now that the spring is in the air.

Rod McKuen, *Seasons in the Sun*

It was like an old person's, dry and thin. "Dad? How are you doing?"

"Pretty good. I'll be out of here in a few weeks."

"You look fine."

"Sure, sure. Everything all right?"

"Yes," I said.

"Oh . . ."

Mom stepped between us and bent over him. "Do you want Mrs. Williams?"

"No. It's gone now."

"They'll bring the shot soon."

"I know."

"Where does it hurt? Try to tell me."

"It's nothing, just gas pains. . . . You called the office this morning?"

"Yes."

"And everything's all right?"

"The deliveries will be on schedule—don't worry about it."

"What about Mary's cold? She had a bad cold last week."

"That was long ago, Leo."

"I told her to go home, but she wouldn't. Sitting at the typewriter with this bad cold."

"She's fine, darling. You mustn't worry so much."

"Everything goes to pieces when I'm not there. . . ."

Mom glanced at me. "Davy, your father can't see you on that side."

I came around to the other side of the bed and smiled at him. "Benjamin?" he asked.

"No," I said. "It's Davy."

"Funny . . . you looked like your uncle. I was dreaming of a boat. Steerage. My father came over in steerage."

"I'm glad to see you, Dad."

"If he told the story once, he told it a million times. The crowded conditions. People got sick and one of the kids died. Ben would always get so upset by that story."

"Dad, I want to . . ."

He gazed at me. "You look so much like your uncle. . . . Can I have some water?" Mom put a straw in the water glass and lifted his head from the pillow. "Thank you."

"Don't talk," she said. "Let us do the talking."

"What's the matter? I can't visit with my own family?"

"Just try to rest."

He closed his eyes and she sat there holding his hand, her face transformed by a look I had never seen before. As though he were her child, someone small and sick who couldn't do anything for himself. She moistened her handkerchief in the glass of water and wiped his forehead. Then she watched him as he slept. He mumbled something and she said, "Shh, darling. I'm here." And I knew that I had no place in that room, or in their lives. They were far beyond me, in a world I couldn't enter, and the fact that it was my own doing didn't help me. I had come too late.

David feels that he should be emotionally involved; yet he realizes there is such a great distance between himself and his parents that he cannot help or comfort them at this difficult time in their lives. Imagine that after his visit to the hospital David sees his girlfriend. Write, in David's own words, what he tells her about his visit and the feelings it generated in him.

Judy's Letter

Dear Annie,

I know you must have been very shocked when you heard about Walter, it was a shock to me and I knew what was coming, after you seen him in August he was in hospital till about the first Sept and came home he had picked up a little or maybe it was just a bit happy at being home. it wasnt to long before he started to go down grade again we were going to the doctor. each time it was different pills and medicine he wasn't getting any better by Nov he was really sick he could hardly get dressed by him self and he slept down stairs on the couch a lot during the day his strength was just about gone, he was trying so hard to breathe and I was trying so hard to keep him. it was heart breaking to see him like that he developed a pain in his stomach so I had the Dr. over I heard Walter asking for some thing to take the pain away, the Dr said I am going to put you in the hospital for a few days, my brother & sister inlaw took him over on friday and he was gone the next friday, I seen him every day and spent the afternoon with him. about wednesday I could see a change in Walter he knew me and talked to me, I dont think he knew if I was there or not on thursday some times I thought he did, on wednesday I whispered in his ear I love you so much, he said you can say that again and he squeezed my hand, he held my hand all the time I was there on Wed. I was there all afternoon on thursday and that night I was very uneasy so about 10 PM, by brother took me over and we stayed till twelve there was a big chang by that time, the nurse said we should go home and try and get some rest and she would call us if there was more change at 2 am the phone rang she told us to come over, so I was beside him till he left me at twelve minutes past six, it was still dark out side he went easy just like in a deep sleep. I know he was happy to go he couldnt have gone on like that God was good to release him and take him home with him, I am so lonely and this house seems so big and quiet, I dont know how long I can live here.

Well Walter and I had a long happy life together, but if it had been twice that long it wouldn't have been long enough for me he was always very precious to me from the first time I met him I loved him very dearly, all his days we had together.

Much love always,

Judy

Death can be recorded in many ways. Judy writes of her husband's death with warmth, compassion, and infinite love. In contrast, an obituary reports only the unemotional facts. Write Walter's obituary as it might appear in your local newspaper. Invent any details you need to make it look authentic.

In this chapter you have read several fictional accounts and one real-life description of the ways people face death. The following magazine articles report what some doctors believe to be the emotional and mental stages that people pass through in dying.

Out of Darkness

A group of medical and theological students, nurses and social workers gathers every other Wednesday in a room at the University of Chicago's Billings Hospital to learn about dying. The seminar's instructors are indisputable authorities on the subject. They are all terminal patients in the hospital who have volunteered to share with strangers the last and most terrifying experience of life. . . . In four years the seminar has heard from 150 patients; there have been only three refusals. The author now understands why. "To live on borrowed time," she writes, "to wait in vain for the doctors to make their rounds, lingering on from visiting hours to visiting hours, looking out of the window, hoping for a nurse with some extra time for a chat, this is the way many terminally ill patients pass their time. Is it then surprising when such a patient is intrigued by a strange visitor who wants to talk to her about her own feelings?" From these feelings, freely given, the seminar has been

able to trace the five successive stages of life's last journey:

▶ The dying patient's first reaction is **denial:** "No, not me." The response serves an important function. Writes Dr. Kübler-Ross: "It allows the patient to collect himself and, with time, mobilize other, less radical defenses."

▶ Denial eventually yields to deep **anger:** "Why me?" A 50-year-old dentist, dying of cancer, told the seminar: "An old man whom I have known ever since I was a little kid came down the street. He was 82 years old, and he is of no earthly use as far as we mortals can tell. And the thought hit me strongly, now why couldn't it have been old George instead of me?"

▶ Resentment is succeeded in turn by **bargaining**—a campaign, often undetectable, to somehow stay execution of sentence. A difficult patient may abruptly turn cooperative; the reward he seeks for good behavior is an extension of life. The author cites

the poignant case of an opera singer, her face consumed by a fatal malignancy, who begged for a chance to sing one last time; thus, death would have to wait. She did—and it did.

▶ After the bargaining stage, the patient generally sinks into a profound **depression.** This stage, the author believes, has a positive side. The patient is weighing the fearful price of death, preparing himself to accept the loss of everything and everyone he loves.

▶ The fifth and final stage is **acceptance,** when at last the condemned patient bows to his sentence. "I think this is the miracle," the seminar was told by one woman who had steadfastly refused to accept the fact of her impending death. "I am ready now and not even afraid any more." She died the following day.

Dr. Kübler-Ross warns that the patient's final resignation should not be mistaken for euphoria, as it sometimes is. Passivity is a better description: "His circle of interest diminishes.

He wishes to be left alone or at least not stirred up by news and problems of the outside world." The patient's family often misinterpret this state as rejection. "We can be of greatest service to them," the author reasons, "if we help them understand that only patients who have worked through their dying are able to detach themselves slowly and peacefully in this manner. It is during this time that the family needs the most support, the patient perhaps the least."

Even after acceptance of the inevitable, it is the rare terminal case who abandons hope. When that occurs, says the author, death is imminent. . . .

Dr. Kübler-Ross concludes that the patient who is not officially told that his illness is fatal always discovers the truth anyway, and may resent the deception, however well meant. . . . It is not death they fear, but dying, a process almost as painful to see as to endure, and one on which society—and even medicine—so readily turns its back.

Time, October 10, 1969

List Dr. Kübler-Ross' five stages of dying, using only a one-word heading for each stage. Review the various selections in this chapter and pick out phrases that you think illustrate each stage.

While Dr. Kübler-Ross studied the feelings of terminally ill patients, the following article is about Dr. Noyes' studies of the experiences of people who faced *almost*-fatal encounters with sudden death. Dr. Noyes' findings are similar in some ways to Dr. Kübler-Ross', but in other ways the results are startling.

A Bliss Before Dying?

"A dazzling prismatic effulgence* cleared my vision," the young poet recalled. "Not only did I see and hear harmony, but I understood everything." A Swiss geology professor described it this way: "Elevated and harmonious thoughts dominated and united individual images and, like magnificent music, a

_____
* great brightness

divine calm swept through my soul." Such were the impressions of these particular individuals of that climactic human experience, a close brush with death— the poet in a near drowning and the professor in a 66-foot fall from a mountain peak.

Dr. Russell Noyes, a psychiatrist who has studied some 80 such almost-fatal encounters with sudden death, has discovered that many of the victims' recollections follow a distinct, almost predictable pattern. According to Noyes, an associate professor of psychiatry at the University of Iowa College of Medicine, this pattern can be broken down into three chronological divisions: resistance, review and transcendence.

In the first stage,

Noyes explains, the victim's realization that death is imminent precipitates a violent struggle to gain control of the situation so that he can remain alive. "Where even a slight possibility of survival remains," says Noyes, "alertness to the dangerous environment is enhanced, and energy available for both physical and mental activity may be enormously increased." If the danger is not overcome, the victim often surrenders to a feeling of passive resignation, which in turn leads to a sensation of profound tranquillity.

At this point, notes Noyes, the person may experience a peculiar split between body and mind—a state that apparently permits him to "watch" his own death with a feeling of detachment. At the same time, perhaps because he has temporarily ruled out a future for himself, the victim switches to concentration on the past. As he enters the "review" stage, says Noyes, he often sees what seems to be his past life laid out before him. Vivid memories, usually of a pleasant nature, flash through his mind in rapid succession, somewhat like a speeded-up movie. In one case, a nurse who had suffered a near-fatal allergic reaction to penicillin recalled scenes from her childhood in bright colors: a favorite doll with blue glass eyes, a shiny red bicycle.

Joy: A third of the cases Noyes has studied claim they have experienced the "review" stage. A smaller number —he estimates about 25 per cent—came still closer to death and entered the third stage, transcendence. In this final phase, says Noyes, the person sometimes feels as though he had slipped beyond the restrictive boundaries of past and future. "It was the most perfect state of easeful joy that I ever experienced," wrote the nearly drowned poet. "There was no sadness or sickness from which I wished to escape." For the mountain-climbing professor, "everything was transfigured, as though by a heavenly light, and everything was beautiful without grief, without anxiety and without pain . . . I became ever more surrounded by a splendid blue heaven with delicate roseate and violet cloudlets."

Typical descriptions of this last stage, says Noyes, include flashes of light, visions, ecstasy, the presence of "an outside force" and, in a few instances, a sense of fusion with nature. These experiences, Noyes theorizes, may well be influenced by individual conceptions of the hereafter—but so far, he notes, few of the victims studied have reported visions of hell and damnation. "All the stages don't always develop," Noyes adds, but most victims recall at least an altered mental state in which time slows down and perceptions seem more acute than usual. . . .

Of the cases Noyes has studied to date, he interviewed twenty in person. Sixty others were culled from medical journals and letters from persons who had read about his research or seen the ads he placed in mountain-climbing journals. The study is still far from complete, but what has impressed Noyes already about his findings is that no matter what the threat of death —from loss of footing to loss of oxygen—the subjects tell much the same story.

Newsweek, May 6, 1974

List all the pleasant images of your life which might flash before your eyes if you had an almost-fatal encounter with sudden death. Group these images into some order, such as: most important to least important; people, places, events; or milestones in chronological order.

If you happen to find yourself in this predicament, here's a tongue-in-cheek guide to the dos and dont's called for by such occasions. Beware—there won't be any second chances!

Etiquette for an Execution

J. P. Donleavy

Relax and wait. Most things will be taken care of for you. And generally there will be accorded some measure of courtesy regarding your last wishes. The major part of your time will be spent praying or playing games and cards with your keepers. During this period it is extremely bad form to be caught cheating, since your opponents will, if they can, be trying to keep you happy and winning if possible.

Usually you will be fatally outnumbered and with no chance of escape you may as well comport yourself with quietude and dignity. Of course, some do attempt to present a cavalier touch with a phony feeble outburst of bombast.

"I say there, you chaps, can't we get this . . . thing over with, I haven't all day."

But wailing cowardice, groveling and begging does stir up horror in your on-lookers and makes your death not a nice thing to witness, albeit folk shouldn't be there trying to enjoy it anyway. However, it is simply not done to have people have to drag, carry and tug you along to your place of dispatch.

Don't try to get friendly with your executioners or strike up poses of bon-homie*. The proper posture is to be possessed of a small measure of unblinking arrogance with shoulders held well back, chin up and the arms firmly placed unflappingly at the sides. Above all never succumb to the hangdog look and allow the hands to come up in front of your person and there be wrung till the knuckles glow with whiteness. It will make everybody around you painfully ill at ease.

* good fellowship

In cases where your keepers have wrapped your wrists in thongs behind your back, request if this restraining device can be omitted. However, in countries where they jump on you without warning while you are asleep and tie you up, you are certain to struggle at first till you wake sufficiently to find it is only the guys who have come to execute you. Ask calmly to be unhanded and walk purposefully forward but avoid being overtly military about it. A loose leg movement from the hips, as a manner of motion, is suggested.

While making your way to your place of execution do be on the lookout for folk who may be visibly shaken by the spectacle. Only a passing smile or nod from you can convey poignant reassurance. Watching another being dispatched is for some people the supreme entertainment and for your own peace of mind it may

be as well to avoid their sickly thrill expectant smiles. If you are of a hypochondriacal tendency it is quite a relief not to have to worry about ailing anymore, as impending execution really knocks [the stuffings] out of your daily complaints like no other remedy can and it may result in your reaching the best physical condition of a lifetime.

In the same tone as "Etiquette for an Execution," write a list of at least six rules of good behavior for one of the following situations:
  facing the assistant principal
  facing your parents after wrecking their car
  facing the waiter on discovering that you cannot pay for the meal you just ate.

1. Read one of the following books and discuss it with other members of the class who read the same book. As a group, prepare an oral report relating the book to any of the problems discussed in this chapter. When appropriate, use visual aids to make your report more interesting.

Run Softly, Go Fast by Barbara Werbsa
A Separate Peace by John Knowles
Death Be Not Proud by John Gunther
The Loved One by Evelyn Waugh
Love Story by Erich Segal
The Pigman by Paul Zindel
Sounder by William Armstrong
A Death in the Family by James Agee

3. Imagine that the boy in "Out, Out—" was a classmate of yours. Make up an *in memoriam* page for your class yearbook as a tribute to him. Cut a picture from a magazine, make up a name for him, and invent a complete personality. Paste up the page layout as exactly as you can.

Activities

2. Almost every high-school yearbook includes a page dedicated to a student who has died during the school year. In our minds, we associate death with "other people"—the old, or those engaged in dangerous occupations. However, every year teenagers die in accidents, from terminal diseases, and so on. Research the statistics on causes and probabilities of death for different age groups. Make your own graphs and charts to demonstrate these statistics before the class. For source material you may consider the "Vital Statistics" section of an almanac or write to:

Division of Vital Statistics
National Center for Health Statistics
Public Health Service
U.S. Dept. of Health, Education, and
Welfare

4. Adapt the excerpt from *Run Softly, Go Fast* to dramatic form. With a group of classmates, choose the best piece of the ones written by the class in response to that selection and use it as an epilogue to your drama. Perform your play before the class.

5. Write a letter of sympathy to Judy whose husband died or to the parents of the boy in "Out, Out—".

8. Write your own obituary notice after referring to the assignment that you wrote at the beginning of this chapter. Check the obituaries in your local newspaper or in *Time* for models.

6. You are an editor of a medical journal dealing with the psychology of dying. You have decided to publish the *Time* and *Newsweek* articles in your journal. Write a brief foreword to the articles in which you compare the similarities and differences between the two.

7. Interview people whose occupations have brought them in contact with death, such as undertakers, medical personnel, or war veterans. Ask questions to determine their feelings toward death and (in the case of undertakers and doctors) how they go about consoling families that have experienced a death.

9. Organize a debate on euthanasia (mercy killing). Each side should research its position by referring to the school library card catalog. The *Readers' Guide to Periodical Literature* is also useful for finding magazine articles on the subject. Do not overlook human sources: family, religious leaders, lawyers, and doctors can all contribute valuable moral and legal points of view.

10. With four members of the class, pick a character from the selections you have read in this chapter. Imagine this person going through Dr. Kübler-Ross' five stages of death. Each group member can then write a one-page entry in the character's diary which reflects one of the stages of dying so that the total group effort will record all five stages.

6
Living
with Death

The many different ways in which the living dispose of the bodies of the dead have their beginnings in religious belief and social custom. The ancient Egyptians, for example, were so concerned about ensuring a happy afterlife for the dead that the process of preparing a dead body for proper burial often lasted seventy days. Although today's funeral preparations are not as elaborate as the Egyptians', families still perform certain religious or traditional rituals in burying their dead.

Write down what you think is necessary for a proper funeral. Consider step by step everything that a family does from the moment of a relative's death to the time of burial. With the entire class, discuss what each student has written and note on the blackboard the customs that differ from one social group to the next. Try to determine how these customs began and why they are performed.

At one time, family members were responsible for every detail of a relative's funeral. Now, according to a *Newsweek* article, most Americans die in hospitals where they are prepared for burial in an assembly-line process by uncaring strangers.

How America Lives with Death

Newsweek, April 6, 1970

It was 8:15 Wednesday morning, and the patient in room 249 was dying, on schedule. On Monday, nurses had moved him to a private room; it is easier to close a door on the dead than to curtain a corpse in a crowded ward. The morgue attendant had calculated him in the week's projected workload. A memo was posted on the bulletin board in the doctors' lounge: "Dr. Lewis needs eyes." At the morgue, another notice appeared: "Dr. Davis needs kidneys." A red border on the patient's hospital file card signaled the Roman Catholic chaplain. On Tuesday, the chaplain administered the last rites of the church and rubber-stamped the fact on the card. Hospital officials had obtained early permission for an autopsy: the next-of-kin might be out of town at the crucial moment.

By 9 a.m. Wednesday the patient in room 249 was dead. The nurse closed the corpse's eyes and summoned the orderlies.

The physician notified the relatives. Within fifteen minutes, a temporary death certificate had been signed (pending confirmation of cause of death), a "release of personal belongings" form had been completed, and the body had been washed, plugged, trussed, wrapped in sheets and labeled. The morgue attendant loaded the body onto his rolling stretcher, waited considerately for an empty elevator, then rolled it past the maintenance and laundry rooms (by custom, the staff averted their faces) to a morgue icebox in the basement.

At noon on Thursday, autopsy and legal forms completed, room 249's late occupant arrived at the mortuary—minus his eyes and kidneys. He was drained, embalmed, waxed, rouged, shaved, dressed and wheeled into the "slumber room." At 3:30 p.m. on Saturday, after a 35-minute church service, the Duraseal coffin was lowered by machine into the prepurchased cemetery plot and buried.

Every day, more than 5,000 Americans die. A favored few succumb at home; . . . 75 per cent—like the patient in room 249—are routinely processed out of existence through the labyrinthine* corridors of crowded institutions. But wherever or however death comes, Americans try to handle it with cool, efficient dispatch. Death in America is no longer a metaphysical mystery or a summons from the divine. Rather, it is an engineering problem for death's managers—the physicians, morticians and statisticians in charge of supervising nature's planned obsolescence. To the nation that devised the disposable diaper, the dead are only a bit more troublesome than other forms of human waste.

The way the author uses words in this article creates a shocking, but slightly humorous effect. List the words, phrases, and other details in this article that were used to suggest that death in America is similar to an assembly line in a factory.

* mazelike

Many people specify the exact way in which they wish to be buried, hoping that relatives will honor their requests. Since Americans hire undertakers to bury their dead, how can a family check to make sure that the dead person's funeral requests are carried out perfectly? In this selection from *The American Way of Death,* a dissatisfied Mr. Chelini is suing the undertaker, Mr. Nieri, because the coffin that Mr. Chelini bought for his dead mother did not measure up to the claims made by the undertaker.

FROM The American Way of Death

Jessica Mitford

The case opens with the arrival of Mr. Nieri at the Chelini home. Mr. Melvin Belli, counsel for the plaintiff, is examining:

A. Well, I told him that my mother wanted to be buried where there was no ants or any bugs could get at her.

Q. Had your mother made that request?

A. She made that request.

Q. By the way, was your mother of sound mentality at the time?

A. Oh, yes, very sound. Pretty bright.

Q. Did you tell him anything else?

A. Well, I told him that she had $1500 of her own money, and that I in-

tended to put all that into her funeral, and she had other moneys coming, and I wanted a hermetically sealed casket, because—

Q. You told him that, that you wanted—

A. I told him I wanted the best kind of embalming, and I wanted her put in a hermetically sealed casket.

Q. Did you know what a hermetically sealed casket was at that time?

A. Well, I know that it was a casket that no air or no water could get into. . . .

Q. . . . Did you have any further conversation with him?

A. Well, we talked about the embalming, how long he could preserve it, he says, "Practically forever," he says, "We got a new method of embalming that we will put on her, and she will keep almost forever." . . .

Then the next day he told me that I would have to come down to his establishment, and pick out a casket. . . .

Q. And you went down there?

A. My wife and I went down there.

Q. And when you got down there, did you have a further conversation with him?

A. Well, yes, he took me down in the basement there where he had all these caskets, and he told me to look them all over, and we picked out what we thought was the best casket in the house. . . . He quoted me a price, then he says, "Well, that will be $875, that will include everything, everything in connection with the whole funeral." . . . So, from what he told me, this casket was the best—it seemed very reasonable, so I told him that we would select that. . . .

Mr. Chelini was, it appears, the exceptional—nay, perfect—funeral customer. Not only did he gladly and freely choose the most expensive funeral available in the Nieri establishment; he also contracted for a $1,100 crypt in the Cypress Lawn mausoleum. . . .

At first glance, it seems like a frightful stroke of bad luck that Mr. Chelini, of all people, should be in court charging negligence and fraud against his erstwhile friend the undertaker, asserting that "the remains of the said Caroline Chelini were permitted to and did develop into a

rotted, decomposed and insect and worm infested mess." Yet the inner logic of the situation is perhaps such that *only* a person of Mr. Chelini's persuasion in these matters would ever find himself in a position to make such a charge; for who else would be interested in ascertaining the condition of a human body after its interment?

Break into groups and read aloud the short scene presented here. Next in your group develop Mr. Nieri's case. Improvise a scene in which Mr. Nieri gives testimony. Be prepared to reenact the scene for the class.

Mr. Chelini supposedly bought the most
expensive funeral for his mother.
Most people, however, cannot afford
to be so lavish, and, as Manuel discovers
in this following selection, poverty
can make living with death all the more
difficult.

A Death
in the Sanchez Family

Oscar Lewis

Finally a gray hearse arrived, a half hour
late. Those guys from the funeral parlor
came to do a job and cared nothing about
keeping up appearances or anything. They
were completely indifferent to the grief of
the mourners. It was pure business. Right
off, they wanted to be paid. Consuelo
came over to me and said, "Listen,
Roberto doesn't have enough money. He
needs thirty-five *pesos*. Do you have
any?" Jaime, the shorty, stuck his hand in
his pocket at the same time I did and
handed over twenty *pesos* to my brother.
I gave the rest. Then two of the undertakers picked up the heavy candlesticks
and carried them out. I looked around
for a wreath but nobody had brought one.
There were only a few withered flowers.
And there was only one funeral bus. It
was one of those old public buses, with
seats in rows on each side of the aisle.
The bus was painted black and in fair
condition but inside it was very dirty.

It's a little ironic but even the dead
have their status. The difference in price
decides whether you travel first or second
class. If you pay more, you get an elegant
hearse, a fancy casket, a later model bus
and the mourners are treated with every
consideration. My aunt's funeral was the
very poorest there is. She went second
class right to the end.

A crowd of people, mostly children,
began to get on the bus. Some women
were carrying my aunt's little evergreen
plants to put on the grave. Everybody was
pushing and rushing around, children
were whining to go with their mothers. It
reminded me of the pilgrimages we used
to make to the shrine in Chalma.

The bus filled up quickly and someone yelled, "No, no, the kids can't go.
Just adults! All children get out!"
Seats were set aside for the mourning
relatives and when my name was called, I
got on the bus with María.

I had not intended to go to the cemetery, but everyone expected me to so I
did. The day I buried my first wife, Paula,
I swore never to go to another funeral

that was not my own. It's hard for me to describe what a cemetery represents to me. It is not a matter of fear but rather of pain, pain that is deep in the most secret part of my soul. I know myself. I know the kind of traumas I suffered from. Not only my wife's death, but my mother's and my *papá's* second wife, Alicia. I felt them all because my father blamed me for all of them. To this day I can't get his accusing voice out of my mind.

Look, death in itself is something very serious. It's nothing I'd make jokes about. To me, death is final. The end. But even so I have a phobia about being buried. When I die I'd rather they had me standing up, any way at all, but not buried.

It was a long trip to the Dolores cemetery. They drove that hearse like a taxicab, as fast as they could, with the mourners' bus following behind. Nothing like what I saw in California, where the hearse would proceed slowly as though with grief. Nobody in the bus cried on the way there. Some were even smiling as if they were on their way to a picnic.

When we arrived, Roberto and Consuelo got out to take care of the papers. A little later I saw them talking, and then they went over to the driver of the hearse who started up the motor and backed up to the little church opposite the office. I got out and joined them. Four men lowered the casket from the hearse, carried it into the church, and set it down on some benches. My sister spoke to the priest. It seems that before getting down to work, the holy man, out of Christian charity, said, "That will be thirty *pesos*." Consuelo turned to me and made a face. "It's thirty *pesos,* brother." What could I do? I handed it over.

How few priests practice what they preach! I'm so steeped in business nowadays I can see clearly that the priests, too, are doing nothing but business. If some poor guy arrives, the priest pays no attention to him, but if one arrives in a nice automobile it's, "Yes, my son, here and, yes, my son, there." They buy him God's pardon and give him an automatic pass to Paradise. If you get married in church and you want a carpet, it'll cost you so much. If you want flowers, so much more. Singing? So much. There's a price list for everything, with a different charge for Purgatory, Heaven, and Paradise. . . .

After the Mass the undertakers came over to Roberto and said, "If you want us to take your relative as far as the canyon it will cost you another seventy-five *pesos*."

Buzzards, that's all they are . . . buzzards, I said to myself. I made up my mind not to give them another *centavo*. There was no money left anyway. When they saw that it was impossible to squeeze out any more, the men from the funeral parlor resigned themselves and took the body out of the church. They loaded it on the hearse again and we started off to my aunt's last resting place.

Chuang Tze on Death

When Chuang Tze was about to die, his disciples expressed a wish to give him a splendid funeral. But Chuang Tze said, "With heaven and earth for my coffin and shell; with the sun, moon, and stars as my burial regalia; and with all creation to escort me to the grave,—are not my funeral paraphernalia ready to hand?"

"We fear," argued the disciples, "lest the carrion kite* should eat the body of our Master"; to which Chuang Tze replied, "Above ground I shall be food for kites; below I shall be food for mole-crickets and ants. Why rob one to feed the other?"

* a kind of hawk

Chuang Tze did not care about what kind of funeral he received. Write a short but detailed description of the kind of funeral that you personally would like to have.

Unlike Chuang Tze who did not care how his body was buried, Shah Jahan, a Mogul Emperor of India during the 1600's, cared very much how his beloved wife, who died giving birth to her thirteenth child, should be buried. In 1632, he ordered a mausoleum to be built for her. Mainly made of white marble inlaid with semiprecious stones, the Taj Mahal, as it came to be called, rises 243 feet above elaborate gardens and pools. It took more than 20,000 workers eleven years to build the mausoleum itself, and a total of twenty-two years to complete the whole complex.

"The Story of Kisagotami" is a Buddhist parable about a grieving mother who learns from the Buddha how to accept the death of her young son.

The Story of Kisagotami

Kisagotami became in the family way, and when the ten months were completed, gave birth to a son. When the boy was able to walk by himself, he died. The young girl, in her love for it, carried the dead child clasped to her bosom, and went about from house to house asking if any one would give her some medicine.

Kisagotami went to Gautama, and doing homage to him, said, "Lord and master, do you know any medicine that will be good for my boy?" Gautama replied, "I know of some." She asked, "What medicine do you require?" He said, "I want a handful of mustard seed." The girl promised to procure it for him, but Gautama continued, "I require some mustard seed taken from a house where no son, husband, parent, or slave has died." The girl said, "Very good," and went to ask for some at the different houses, carrying the dead body of her son astride on her hip. The people said, "Here is some mustard seed, take it." Then she asked, "In my friend's house has there died a son, a husband, a parent, or a slave?" They replied, "Lady, what is this that you say! The living are few, but the dead are many." Then she went to other houses, but one said, "I have lost a son"; another, "I have lost my parents"; another, "I have lost my slave." At last, not being able to find a single house where no one had died, from which to procure the mustard seed, she began to think,

"This is a heavy task that I am engaged in. I am not the only one whose son is dead. In the whole of the Savatthi country, everywhere children are dying, parents are dying." Thinking thus, she acquired the law of fear, and putting away her affection for her child, she summoned up resolution, and left the dead body in a forest; then she went to Gautama and paid him homage. He said to her, "Have you procured the handful of mustard seed?" "I have not," she replied; "the people of the village told me, 'The living are few, but the dead are many.'"

Some time afterwards, when Kisagotami was one day engaged in the performance of her religious duties, she observed the lights in the houses now shining, now extinguished, and began to reflect, "My state is like these lamps." Gautama, who was then in the Gandhakuti building, sent his sacred appearance to her, which said to her, just as if he himself were preaching, "All living beings resemble the flame of these lamps, one moment lighted, the next extinguished.

A parable is a story which illustrates a moral truth. Carefully reread "The Story of Kisagotami" and in a sentence or two write down the moral truth which Gautama Buddha taught to the young girl.

If you have ever read the inscriptions on tombstones in an old graveyard, you know that epitaphs are written in memory of the persons buried there. Often people write their own epitaphs, but more often epitaphs are composed by the person who carves the stone or by a surviving member of the family. Here are some famous and not-so-famous epitaphs.

Epitaphs

Under the wide and starry sky,
Dig the grave and let me lie.
Glad did I live and gladly die,
And I laid me down with a will.

This be the verse you grave for me:
"Here he lies where he longed to be,
Home is the sailor, home from the sea,
And the hunter's home from the hill."

Robert Louis Stevenson

A m Short, O Lord, of praising thee,
N othing I can do is right;
N eedy and naked, poor I be,

S hort, Lord, I am of sight,
H ow short I am of love and grace;
O f everything I am short,
R enew me, then I'll follow Peace
T hrough good and bad report.

Ann Short

The Body of
B Franklin Printer,
(Like the Cover of an Old Book
Its Contents torn out
And stript of its Lettering & Gilding)
Lies here, Food for Worms.
But the Work shall not be lost;
For it will, (as he believ'd) appear
once more,
In a new and more elegant Edition
Revised and Corrected
By the Author.

Shall We All Die?
We Shall Die All.
All Die Shall We?
Die All We Shall.
Anonymous

Cast a cold eye
On life, on death.
Horseman, pass by!
William Butler Yeats

Write an epitaph, either humorous or serious, that you would like to appear on your gravestone.

1. If there is an old cemetery within traveling distance of your home, visit it to study the gravestones and other monuments. Search out interesting epitaphs, make sketches or tombstone rubbings, or take photographs of the monuments, and make notes on the different ways that Americans memorialize their dead. Report your findings to the class.

Activities

2. *The American Way of Death* describes the various, often extravagant, burial customs of Americans. Americans also spend a great deal of money to bury their pets. Use the *Readers' Guide to Periodical Literature* or write to Pet Cemeteries to research this growing practice. Report your findings to the class.

3. "How America Lives with Death" and "A Death in the Sanchez Family" describe the cold, businesslike, routine ways in which some people bury the dead. Write an editorial for your local newspaper, stating your opinion about this practice.

4. Write a skit showing a meeting between Chuang Tze and Shah Jahan. Imagine that the Shah has brought his building plans for the Taj Mahal to Chuang Tze to seek his approval and advice. Prepare costumes for the two characters, keeping in mind that Shah Jahan was an extremely wealthy monarch and that Chuang Tze was a religious leader and philosopher. Perform your skit before the class.

5. "The Story of Kisagotami" is a parable illustrating a moral truth. With two classmates, list several proverbs and morals and then choose one and use it as the basis to write a parable.

6. Write your own will and last testament. Give reasons for each of your bequests.

7. Research how other cultures dispose of their dead. Select one of the following topics for a short report:
—the old Hindu custom of *suttee*
—Greek funeral games as described in Homer's *Iliad*, Book 23
—the catacombs
—the Egyptian pyramids and mummification
—Eskimo traditions concerning death
—American Indian traditions
—the origin of the word *mausoleum*
—Parsee (Parsi) burial traditions
—other burial traditions (Oriental, African, South American, etc.)

8. The Taj Mahal is probably the most beautiful monument to the dead in the world. Bring in to class pictures of other famous tombs, such as Hadrian's Tomb, the tomb of Pope Julius II, Grant's Tomb, the Tomb of the Unknown Soldier, the Arc de Triomphe, the *tholos* or *beehive* tombs of Mycenae, the tomb of Tutankhamen, or the tomb of John F. Kennedy. Be prepared to deliver a short description of the monument to the class.

Adieu my friends

7 The Search

for Immortality

Something that is immortal never dies, but lives forever. People have always sought immortality in one way or another: the early Spanish explorers mistakenly believed that somewhere in the Americas they would find the Fountain of Eternal Youth; at one time in Europe, there lived a countess who tried to stay young forever by using the blood of young girls as if it were facial cream; today, some scientists propose extending life indefinitely by freezing living bodies to be revived some time in the future. But, realistically, most people search for immortality through their work, which will live on after their personal deaths. In this sense, immortality means not being forgotten by future generations.

Write a sentence or two on a half sheet of paper, stating by what accomplishments you would like most to be remembered. Do not sign it. After all the papers have been collected, someone should read them aloud to the class while someone else keeps a tally on the blackboard to determine which ideas are mentioned most often.

The search for immortality has occupied
the minds of peoples all over the world.
In these two myths, the first from the
island of Madagascar and the second
from ancient Greece, we learn that
immortality can have its drawbacks.

The Moon or the Banana

Barbara Stanford with Gene Stanford

One day God asked the first human couple, who then lived in heaven, what kind
of death they wanted—that of the moon or that of the banana. The couple
wondered what the difference was, so God explained: The banana puts forth
shoots that take its place and the moon itself comes back to life.

   The couple considered for a long time before they made their choice. If they
decided to be childless, they could avoid death for themselves, but they would also
be very lonely and would themselves have to carry out all of the work and
would not have anyone to work and strive for.

   So they asked God for children, well aware of the consequences of their
choice. And their request was granted.

   Since that time man's time on this earth is very short.

Tithonus and the Goddess of the Dawn

One morning, as Aurora, the Goddess of the Dawn, rose to bring light to the earth, she saw a young prince of Troy walking through the palace gardens. In all her travels over the face of the earth, she had never seen a more handsome young man. His name was Tithonus, and Aurora promptly carried him off to Olympus.

Before the throne of Zeus and in the presence of the other gods, the two were married, and for a wedding gift Aurora begged Zeus to grant immortality to her new husband. Zeus grumbled at the idea, but he granted her request anyway. Tithonus then began to eat the food of the gods, dress like a god, and live with Aurora in a shining palace on Mount Olympus.

Not too many years passed before Aurora noticed that Tithonus was changing. To her horror, Aurora realized that, although she had made sure that her husband would never die, she had forgotten to request that he also remain eternally young like herself and the rest of the gods. As Tithonus grew older year by year, his hair slowly turned white and wrinkles destroyed his handsome face. Aurora pleaded with Zeus to restore her husband's youth, but Zeus would not be moved. Finally Tithonus grew so weak that he could no longer move his arms and legs. He began to pray for death, but his mind had become so dull that he jabbered on and on, making no sense at all.

Aurora was embarrassed by the appearance of her husband and locked him up in a room of her palace. One day guests at the palace wondered what the strange noise was that came from beyond a door. Aurora said it was only her husband and agreed to let her guests see Tithonus. She opened the door and there in the corner of the room, instead of a man, was an insect. Out of pity or disgust, Aurora had transformed the shrunken, but immortal body of Tithonus into a grasshopper.

These two myths present reasons why humankind cannot achieve individual physical immortality. In a sentence or two state these reasons. Which of the two myths hints at another form of immortality? In one sentence, state that alternative form.

The Steele women: six generations without a gap

The oldest woman is 100 and the youngest ten months—a hearty enough span of years—but what is truly remarkable about the six ladies in Alfred Eisenstaedt's picture is that they are members of six generations of the same family in one uninterrupted line, from Trina Roxanne Byerly to her great-great-great-grandmother, Mrs. Roxanne Kennedy Steele. In between are Trina's mother Shirley Ann, 19; grandmother Rita Hall, 37; great-grandmother Geneva Beachnau, 53; and great-great-grandmother Stella Godwin, 74. All six live within a one-hundred-mile radius of the 90-acre farm in the flatlands of southern Alabama where Mrs. Steele, now the matriarch of a clan so vast that no one has counted it, was born.

On Borrowed Time is a play about Julian Northrup, called Gramps, who does not want to die because he wants to continue to care for his orphaned grandson, Pud. Gramps' determination to stay alive is strengthened by his dislike of his sister-in-law, Demetria, who plans to adopt Pud so that she can get her hands on his inheritance. The entire conflict is complicated by the arrival of Mr. Brink, who is the messenger of Death. He has come to carry Gramps off, but Gramps succeeds in tricking Mr. Brink and trapping him up in an apple tree from which he cannot climb down without Gramps' permission. As long as Mr. Brink is trapped in the tree, no one in the world can die except by touching the tree or by eating an apple from it. To prevent this from happening accidentally, Gramps has hired workmen to build a high fence around the tree.

Before the scene opens, Demetria calls in the family doctor and lawyer to witness what she claims is Gramps' madness. Since Mr. Brink is invisible to everyone but Gramps and Pud, Demetria thinks it will be easy to have Gramps put away in an asylum.

The scene begins with Demetria talking to the workmen while she awaits the arrival of the doctor and lawyer.

FROM On Borrowed Time

Paul Osborn

AT [CURTAIN] RISE: *Three* WORKMEN *are building fence.* TWO *are stretching barbed-wire.* ONE *is settling post at top of hill, right.* DEMETRIA *enters from house, goes to gate, looks out, goes to* WORKMEN. BRINK *is invisible.*

DEMETRIA (*to* WORKMAN): Here you, come here.

WORKMAN (*crossing down to her*): Yes, ma'am.

DEMETRIA: Has Mr. Northrup told any of you men why he's building this fence?

WORKMAN: Well, not exactly, ma'am. It's to keep people away from the tree.

DEMETRIA: Why?

WORKMAN: He says if we touch the tree we are in danger.

DEMETRIA: Danger of what?

WORKMAN: Well, I'm not sure, ma'am, I thought he said we were in danger of our lives.

DEMETRIA: That's very interesting. That's what he said to me too. (*She motions* WORKMAN *away, as* DR. EVANS *and* MR. PILBEAM *enter through gate right.*) Ah, Doctor Evans, Mr. Pilbeam, how do you do? I'm glad you could come. (EVANS *has crossed to porch.*) Julian is just around the corner burying his dog.

EVANS (*going to her down center*): What does he want us for?

DEMETRIA: He doesn't want you, gentlemen. It was I who asked you to come up. I want you to meet someone.

PILBEAM (*right of* DEMETRIA): Who?

DEMETRIA: A friend of Julian's—a Mr. Brink.

EVANS: I'm rather busy right now, Miss Riffle.

DEMETRIA: I appreciate that, Doctor, but I thought you would like to meet this friend of Julian's.

EVANS: Well, all right, where is he?

DEMETRIA: Well, just at the moment, he's up in the apple tree.

(*Pause. They look at her surprised, then look up into tree.* DEMETRIA *stands watching them in silence.*)

PILBEAM (*back to her*): Er—where did you say he was?

DEMETRIA: Right up in that apple tree.

(*They glance up again.*)

EVANS (*crossing up left*): I don't see anyone up there.

(*Crossing down left.*)

DEMETRIA: Oh, no. You can't see him. He's invisible.

PILBEAM: What?

DEMETRIA: He's invisible—You see, a short while after Julian got Mr. Brink up there, Betty, the old dog, saw him and barked at him. Mr. Brink didn't like that so he became invisible. And right after that, Betty touched her nose to the tree and dropped over dead. Julian and Pud are burying her now.

EVANS: What is this anyway?

PILBEAM: Is this supposed to be a joke, Miss Riffle?

DEMETRIA: What would you say if I told you I believed it was the Gospel truth?

EVANS: 'Fraid I'd say you were crazy.

DEMETRIA: I would be crazy, wouldn't I? And what if I told you that Mr. Brink is a man, just like you, who goes around taking people away with him when it's time for them to die. Now, if I believed that you'd surely say I was crazy, wouldn't you?

EVANS: I'd say you were positively nuts, Miss Riffle.

DEMETRIA: Yes. Well, I don't believe it—but Julian does.

PILBEAM: Come, come, Miss Riffle, what kind of story is this?

DEMETRIA (*sits in chair left*): An hour ago when I happened to be passing, I saw all those pieces of fence being unloaded from a truck. Naturally, I came back to find out what was going on. Julian told me he was building the fence to keep people away from the tree, because anybody who touched the tree would die.

PILBEAM: Die?

DEMETRIA (*rises*): And not only that! Touching that tree is the only way anyone can die. There is no more death in the world, Mr. Pilbeam, until Julian lets Mr. Brink come down.

EVANS (*crosses back of* DEMETRIA *to right center*): See here, Miss Riffle, you don't think Northrup really believes this?

DEMETRIA (*to him*): Julian is an old man and he's been through a great deal lately. I think it's perfectly obvious what has happened. His mind has just suddenly snapped. Julian Northrup is as crazy as a loon.

EVANS: No, no, I saw Northrup only day before yesterday. He was as sane as any man could be. He's just an old joker. I've known him for years. . . .
(*Crosses right.*)

DEMETRIA: You have, Doctor Evans. And Mr. Pilbeam has been his lawyer for years. That's why I've asked both of you to come up. I'm not asking you to take my word for it. I'm simply asking you to see Julian and convince yourselves that what I'm saying is true.

PILBEAM (*with a look to* EVANS): If Northrup should be insane, you'd have to take Pud, of course, wouldn't you, Miss Riffle?

DEMETRIA: Naturally. I'm next of kin.

EVANS (*crossing upper center right*): Huh!

PILBEAM: That's what I thought.

DEMETRIA: What do you mean? You don't think I'm making this up about Julian?

PILBEAM: I don't know what to think, Miss Riffle.

DEMETRIA (*two steps to* PILBEAM): Ever since Nellie Northrup died, Mr. Pilbeam, you've tried to stop my adopting Pud. Even though I told you that was her dying wish.

PILBEAM: I simply said no court of law would believe you, Miss Riffle.

DEMETRIA: I guess a court of law will feel different about it, if they realize a young boy is being brought up by a maniac? (EVANS *puts bag down by gate, crosses down center.*) I'll be frank with you, Mr. Pilbeam, I intend to get that boy away from this insane man's house before something terrible happens. Tonight—if possible! (DEMETRIA *crosses to* EVANS.) There is a way of taking care of such cases immediately, isn't there?

(PILBEAM *crosses up center.*)

EVANS: Well, yes. I'll tell you, I'm not a psychiatrist, Miss Riffle, but if I think Northrup's crazy, I'll talk it over with Grimes. He's the head of the asylum.

DEMETRIA: You will talk it over with him tonight?

EVANS (*crossly*): When a person's insane you don't usually let him run around loose.

DEMETRIA: Thank you, Doctor Evans, I'll just ask the workmen to . . . (*She crosses up center to* WORKMEN. GRAMPS *is heard bellowing off stage.*) Just a minute, I think he's coming now. (PILBEAM *crosses right.*)

GRAMPS (*off stage*): Here you, there. (GRAMPS *enters from top of hill right, followed by* PUD. *They come down the walk.*) What........ do you mean by

gettin' so near to that tree? Didn't I tell you to stay away from that tree on peril of your lives?

PUD (*carries spade*): What's the idea?

GRAMPS (*still to* WORKMEN): Now, you fellows, go on back to that truck and get the rest of that fence unloaded. Get a move on.

PUD (*sits by tree*): Get a move on.

(WORKMEN *exit up hill.*)

GRAMPS (*crosses to* DEMETRIA *center*):

Now, what in tarnation are you doin' around here again! I told you . . .

DEMETRIA: It's just that I'm so excited about it, Julian.

GRAMPS: And Pilbeam and Evans, eh? By God, you've told them all about it, haven't you? After I told you not to.

DEMETRIA: Why, no, Julian, I haven't told. . . .

EVANS (*crosses to* GRAMPS): Yes, she's told us all about it. About the tree, the fence, Mr. Brink . . . everything.

GRAMPS (*crosses left*): I might have known it. I might have known it.

EVANS (*follows* GRAMPS *left*): Well, what about it, Northrup? What's the answer?

GRAMPS: Well, it's the truth, Evans. It's just as true as I'm standin' here.

PILBEAM (*laughing*): You mean there's somebody sitting up in that tree?
(*He crosses right center.*)

EVANS: And nobody in the world can die any more?

GRAMPS: Nobody can die any more until I say so, unless they touch that tree, or one of them apples, or Mr. Brink himself.

EVANS (*crossing left*): You're not serious about this, Northrup?

DEMETRIA (*crosses down center*): Of course he is, Doctor. He's perfectly serious, aren't you, Julian?

GRAMPS (*crosses center to* DEMETRIA):

Hey there, what . . . . are you up to anyway?

DEMETRIA: Why, nothing, Julian. I'm just interested. . . .

GRAMPS: Well, I don't want you to go telling anybody else about Mr. Brink. I got him up there and now I gotta figure out what . . . . I'm gonna do with him.

(*Crosses upper center.*)

DEMETRIA: But you don't think you'll be able to keep a thing like this quiet, Julian.

EVANS: Look here, Northrup. Can you talk to Mr. Brink?

GRAMPS: Sure I can talk to him.

EVANS: Have you talked to him since you got him up there?

GRAMPS: Nope. Haven't had time.

EVANS: I wish you'd talk to him now.

GRAMPS: What for? Just so's you can hear him?

EVANS: I just thought, perhaps if you tried to talk to him—well, you'd find out he isn't up there any more.

GRAMPS: Oh, he's up there, all right.

DEMETRIA: Julian, do try to make him talk. I'd love to hear him.

GRAMPS (*crosses to* DEMETRIA): Oh, you would. (*He turns suddenly and stares at* DEMETRIA. *Slight pause.*) Well, by golly, Demmie, I believe I'll let you. I'll let you all hear him. (DEMETRIA *crosses to* PILBEAM *and* EVANS. GRAMPS *goes to tree.* MARCIA *enters from porch.*) Mr. Brink, can you hear me if I don't shout?

BRINK: Sir?

GRAMPS: See, he calls me "Sir." . . .

DEMETRIA (*to* EVANS *and* PILBEAM): There, he thinks someone's answering.

GRAMPS: Well, Mr. Brink, I'm sorry I haven't had more of a chance to talk to you.

(MARCIA *crosses down left.*)

BRINK: Perhaps I shouldn't say it but I'm not extremely upset by that.

GRAMPS: You're not mad at me, are you?

BRINK: I think I might justifiably be allowed some slight irritation.

GRAMPS: Well, I wouldn't have put you there without a....... good reason. I got you up there so this old hellion couldn't get Pud and the money his father left him.

BRINK: I appreciate that your motive was probably sincere.

GRAMPS: Now, I got an idea, and it's goin' to settle once and for all this business of her gettin' Pud. (*He crosses to* DEMETRIA *and pulls her center.*) Come here, you. Stand out here. (*To* BRINK.) You see this old battle-ax here—her name is Demetria Riffle. Have you got anything on your schedule about when you are supposed to snuff her out?

BRINK: Riffle? There's no such name that has come to my attention yet.

GRAMPS: Well, Mr. Brink, I'm goin' to keep you up there until it's time for you to exterminate her.

(GRAMPS *crosses down right.* DEMETRIA *crosses left to* EVANS *and* PILBEAM.)

BRINK: My dear man, that may be a very long time yet. There's no telling how long that woman may hang on.

GRAMPS: Well, that's the way it's goin' to be.

BRINK: But for me to stay here any length of time might be considered by my Superior as a considerable dereliction of duty.

GRAMPS: Can't help it. Them's the terms.

BRINK (*with sigh*): Ah, well! I was afraid of that. Very well, since you and your tree are so tenacious, I shall have to sit here and wait for Miss Riffle's call.

GRAMPS: Do you think you can hold out that long?

BRINK: My dear man, a human life is like the twinkling of an eye to me.

GRAMPS: Oh, yes, I suppose it is. All right, then, Mr. Brink. (GRAMPS *turns back to others.*) Well, there you are! (*They all look at him.*)

DEMETRIA: Julian, I'm sorry for you. I really am.

GRAMPS: Sorry for me? You heard what Mr. Brink said, didn't you?

DEMETRIA: No—I—didn't hear this thing in the tree say anything.

GRAMPS: You didn't? (*Turns to* PILBEAM.) You heard Mr. Brink, Pilbeam?

PILBEAM: I'm sorry, Northrup, I didn't.

GRAMPS (*to* EVANS): Evans!

EVANS (*crosses right center*): No, Northrup, I didn't. . . .

GRAMPS (*frantically*): Marcia! (MARCIA *turns away.* GRAMPS *sits in chair left.*) Well, I'll be a . . . what's the matter? Am I goin' nuts?

EVANS (*crosses to* GRAMPS. *Motions* DEMETRIA, PILBEAM *to cross right*): It's probably just some sort of a dream or something, Northrup. You'll probably get over it in a few weeks and be all right again. (*Crosses right to others.*)

GRAMPS (*softly*): Didn't no one hear what he said? (*Pause.* EVANS *stands looking at him sadly.*)

PUD (*suddenly*): He said a human life was like the twinkling of an eye to him. (*He crosses down to right of* GRAMPS.)

GRAMPS: Ye Gods, that's just what he said! Just what he said! A dream, eh? What else did he say, Pud? (MARCIA *runs into house.*)

PUD: Said he'd have to stay up there 'cause you and the tree was ten . . . ten . . . it was another funny word, Gramps.

GRAMPS: Tenacious!

DEMETRIA (*to* EVANS *and* PILBEAM): See what he's doing to the boy.

GRAMPS: That's just what he said. (*Rises, crosses right.*) You see where that leaves you. (*Pause.*)

DEMETRIA: Guess I'm too dull to hear.

GRAMPS: That's it. Must be. Guess you're all too dull to hear.

PILBEAM: Yes, I guess that must be it. (*They are strangely silent.*)

EVANS (*crosses right center*): I want to show you something, Northrup.

GRAMPS: Hey, there, what are you goin' to do?

EVANS (*starting to tree*): I'm going to eat an apple for you.

GRAMPS (*tripping him*): Hey, you Gol-darned fool, after all I've been tellin' you about them apples. (PUD *hands* GRAMPS *the spade.*) You make one more move toward that tree and I'll brain you. (DEMETRIA *screams.* EVANS *is on ground.*)

EVANS (*quietly*): All right, Northrup. Let me up. I won't go near the tree.

GRAMPS: Gol-darn fool, tryin' to commit suicide! (PUD *sits in chair left.*)

EVANS (*rises*): All right, Northrup. I just wanted to make sure you weren't joking. (*With look to others.*) Are you going to be home a little later this evening, Northrup?

GRAMPS: 'Course I am.

EVANS: I may be over and—er—talk some more about this.

GRAMPS: All right, Evans.

EVANS: Thanks, well . . .

DEMETRIA: I must go.

PILBEAM: Yes. (DEMETRIA *and* PILBEAM *ad lib, as they go off.*)

EVANS: Good-by, Northrup.

GRAMPS: Good-by, Evans. Sorry I had to be rough with you.

EVANS (*picking up bag*): That's all right.

GRAMPS: And don't worry about none of your patients dying for a while, yet.

EVANS (*with a look at* GRAMPS): All right. Good-by, Northrup.
(*He goes out right.*)

GRAMPS (*crosses left, places spade against house*): Well, now, back to work, sonny, back to work.

PUD: Why don't they hear Mr. Brink?

GRAMPS: Don't know, boy, guess they're all too busy.

BRINK (*appears*): Oh, my dear man, that isn't the reason at all.

GRAMPS (*turning to him*): Oh, hello, Mr. Brink. Why is it only Pud and me can hear you, then?

BRINK: I won't go into it now if you don't mind.

GRAMPS: Just as you say, Mr. Brink. One thing I would like to know though.

BRINK: Well?

GRAMPS: You don't think they'll hold it against Pud what I'm doin' to you?

BRINK: I have neither the inclination nor the authorization to dispense information relevant to your inquiry.

PUD (*laughs*): He still talks funny.

GRAMPS: Well, guess I'll have to take that chance. Come on, boy. Say good-by to Mr. Brink.
(*Helps* PUD *up.*)

PUD: 'Bye, Brink.

GRAMPS: Can't you say "Mr. Brink"?

PUD: Good-by, Mr. Brink—excuse me.

BRINK: That's all right—Good-by, Pud.
(GRAMPS *and* PUD *start toward hill.*)

GRAMPS: Well, we gotta get that fence finished tonight, boy.

PUD: We gotta work like [crazy] to do it, though Gramps.

To gain his freedom, Mr. Brink tries to lure Pud into climbing the tree so that he will die. With Pud dead, Mr. Brink believes Gramps would have no further reasons for staying alive. As Pud climbs the fence, he falls before touching the tree and is badly hurt and in terrible pain. The doctor comes and says that Pud will never be able to walk again.

As the scene begins, Gramps, carrying his grandson out toward the apple tree, wants to talk with Mr. Brink.

Scene Six

The tree. Later that night. Moonlight.
AT [CURTAIN] RISE: GRAMPS *is holding* PUD *in his arms. Walks toward tree.* BRINK *is visible.*

PUD: Gramps, I want a heap o' tape, my back hurts, my back.

GRAMPS: Hush, boy, hush for a minute. . . . Mr. Brink?

BRINK: Yes?

GRAMPS: Pud's in terrible pain. Doctor Evans just left and says he'll never be able to walk again. Why did you let him do it, Mr. Brink?

BRINK: My dear man, I didn't mean to hurt the boy. I just meant to take him. It was the only way out. I even waited a day to let the others force you. But you were too clever for them.

GRAMPS: But you could have found some other way than to pick on the boy.

BRINK: It is only through the boy that I

have any hope of getting down from here. He is the only reason that you won't let me come down. What if I should tell you that I'm bound to stay out the time to which you sentenced me? Until Miss Riffle dies?

GRAMPS: You're not, are you? You're not. You don't have to stay up there, do you?

BRINK: No. But I want you to understand how much it means to you, to your whole world, to deny me. Already the world is beginning to feel the pain and sorrow and bewilderment in keeping me here. It is getting worse every hour.

GRAMPS: I guess I tried to bite off more'n I could chew.

BRINK: Much more.

GRAMPS: Will you come down, please, and take us both?

BRINK: Gladly.

GRAMPS: Please come then. Quickly.

PUD: Gramps—

GRAMPS: Yes, boy.

PUD: A heap o' tape. My back hurts so awful—

GRAMPS: Yes, boy. There, there, boy. Just a minute—just a minute. (BRINK *is down.* GRAMPS *holds out* PUD.)

BRINK: No, you are first. (*He touches* GRAMPS' *brow.* GRAMPS *suddenly straightens up.*) Ah, that's better, isn't it?

GRAMPS: Well, well. He was quite a load before. He's light as a feather now. Here, here. (BRINK *bends over and touches* PUD. GRAMPS *lets* PUD *down.* BRINK *and* GRAMPS *bend down to him.*)

PUD (*rousing*): Hello, Mr. Brink.

BRINK: Hello, Pud.

PUD: Are we deaded, Gramps?

GRAMPS: Must be. I feel like a two-year-old. How do you feel?

PUD: I feel like a two-year-old, too, Gramps.

GRAMPS: Mr. Brink, why didn't you tell me it was goin' to be like this?

BRINK: My dear man, I've been trying to tell you how pleasant it is to go with me, but you wouldn't listen.

PUD: You talk so funny, Mr. Brink.

BRINK: Well, never mind me—Come on. Come along!

PUD (*crosses center,* GRAMPS *follows*): But, where we goin', Gramps?

GRAMPS (*stops*): Oh, yes—by golly, that's important. Where are we goin', Mr. Brink?

BRINK: You'll find out.

PUD (*looks at* BRINK): How long will we be there?

BRINK: For eternity.

PUD (*looks at* GRAMPS): How long is eternity, Gramps?

GRAMPS: Right smart piece of time, boy.

PUD: Anyway, we'll be there together, won't we, Gramps?

GRAMPS (*shaking hands with* PUD): You're [darn] right we will be! You're [darn] right!

GRANNY (*off stage*): Juleyun! Juleyun, do you have to use such language in front of the boy?

(*They all look up.*)

GRAMPS: . . . . I thought you said she'd changed! (BRINK *shakes his head disapprovingly.* GRAMPS *throws* GRANNY *a kiss.* GRAMPS *and* PUD *march hand in hand through the gates and up to the ramps.*)

CURTAIN

Suppose Gramps had written a farewell note before he surrendered himself and Pud to Mr. Brink. What would he have said, and to whom would he have addressed it? Write the note.

For Gramps, death brought immortality
of the soul and freedom from earthly
pain. Similarly, this poem by
Emily Dickinson tells of the soul's
journey that begins at death and ends
in eternity.

Because I Could Not Stop for Death

Emily Dickinson

Because I could not stop for Death—
He kindly stopped for me—
The Carriage held but just Ourselves—
And Immortality.

We slowly drove—He knew no haste
And I had put away
My labor and my leisure too,
For His Civility—

We passed the School, where Children strove
At Recess—in the Ring—
We passed the Fields of Gazing Grain—
We passed the Setting Sun—

Or rather—He passed Us—
The Dews drew quivering and chill—
For only Gossamer[1], my Gown—
My Tippet[2]—only Tulle[3]—

We paused before a House that seemed
A Swelling of the Ground—
The Roof was scarcely visible—
The Cornice[4]—in the Ground—

Since then—'tis Centuries—and yet
Feels shorter than the Day
I first surmised the Horses' Heads
Were toward Eternity—

[1] a very light, thin, filmy cloth

[2] a scarflike piece of clothing for the neck and
shoulders, hanging down in front
[3] a thin, fine netting of silk, used for veils and
scarfs
[4] a horizontal molding projecting along the top
of a wall or building

Emily Dickinson's poem imagina-
tively describes the journey from
life on earth to eternity. Write a
sentence for each one of the six
stanzas, describing what is happening at each step of the journey.

Death Speaks:

There was a merchant in Bagdad who sent his servant to the market to buy provisions and in a little while the servant came back, white and trembling, and said, Master, just now when I was in the market place I was jostled by a woman in the crowd and when I turned I saw it was Death that jostled me. She looked at me and made a threatening gesture; now lend me your horse, and I will ride away from this city and avoid my fate. I will go on to Samarra and there Death will not find me. The merchant lent him his horse, and the servant mounted it, and he dug his spurs in its flanks and as fast as the horse could gallop he went. Then the merchant went down to the market place and he saw me standing in the crowd and he came to me and said, Why did you make a threatening gesture to my servant when you saw him this morning? That was not a threatening gesture, I said, it was only a start of surprise. I was astonished to see him in Baghdad, for I had an appointment with him tonight in Samarra.

John O'Hara, *Appointment in Samarra*

Art and literature abound in scenes depicting the figure of Death coming to carry away the living to their graves. Probably for us, the most familiar representation of Death is the Grim Reaper—the skeleton with his cloak and scythe. Understandably, it is not often that Death can be tricked into not carrying off the soul of his intended victim. In this tale from India, a clever and loving wife succeeds in outwitting Yama, the god of death.

Savitri and Death

Barbara Stanford with Gene Stanford

Savitri was the only child of one of the kindest kings of India, and she was the most beautiful, charming, and intelligent woman in the world. In fact, she was so wonderful that all of the eligible men were sure she was a goddess incarnate and would not dare to ask her to marry them. After searching the whole kingdom for a husband for her, the king said to Savitri, "I guess you will have to find a husband for yourself." So he gave her servants and supplies and sent her into the world to find a husband.

Some time later, she returned blushing and smiling. "I have found the man," she said. "He is not rich and powerful, but he is good and kind. He lives in a forest where he cares for his old, blind father. His name is Satyavan."

The sage Narada then came forward. "You have made a good choice, Savitri," he said. "Satyavan is a fine man and his father is really a king whose eyesight and kingdom have been stolen by enemies. But I have very bad news for you. Satyavan is destined to die exactly a year from this day."

Savitri started to cry, but then pulled herself up proudly. "I would rather marry Satyavan for a year than any other man for eternity."

"Perhaps, then, there is hope," said Narada, smiling. "Love like that may be able to conquer death."

Savitri and Satyavan were married and lived happily for a year. But all of this time Savitri prayed and fasted without telling her husband or her in-laws her purpose. At last the day when Satyavan was to die arrived, and Savitri insisted on going with him into the forest. Satyavan would never deny his beloved wife anything and was more than glad to have her company. Suddenly as they were walking through the forest Satyavan fell down in a faint. Savitri held his head in her lap and began to pray again. She seemed to sense a strange presence near her, and concentrating all of her powers, discovered the form of Yama, the god of death. She watched as Yama extracted Satyavan's soul, put it in his noose, and started off for the land of death. Then she got up and followed him.

Yama discovered her coming a short distance behind him and said, "Don't try to follow me. Go back and give your husband's body a good burial."

"I cannot leave my husband," said Savitri. "And I do not believe that that cold body back there is really him. Since you have the real part of my husband, I must follow you, for all my life I have been taught that a wife should follow her husband."

"You are very wise," replied Yama. "I will grant you any wish except the life of your husband."

"If you would, please, give my father-in-law back his sight," Savitri replied, but she did not stop following Yama.

"I thought I told you to go back," Yama said.

"I am sorry," said Savitri, "but I have been taught that one should spend all the time one can in good company, and I perceive that your company is the finest there is."

Yama was very pleased by this, for usually mortals were afraid of him and

could not see his good qualities. So he offered Savitri another wish.

"It would make me very happy if my father could have a son, for I am his only child," she replied.

"Granted," replied Yama. "In fact, he shall have a hundred sons. And now you really must go back." But Savitri kept on following him.

"There is so much I can learn from you," she pleaded. "Why should I return to ordinary mortals when your company is so much better?" Yama was so pleased by this that he offered Savitri still another boon, as long as she did not ask for the life of her husband.

"Well, I guess I would like to have a hundred sons for myself," she replied.

"You certainly shall have them," said Yama. "And now will you please go back? You are certainly the most faithful wife I have ever met."

"You are right," said Savitri. "I am a faithful wife and I will never have anything to do with any man except my husband. So I must ask you one more question. If you carry off my husband in death, how will I ever have the hundred sons you have promised me?"

"You win," said Yama as he loosened his noose from around the soul of Satyavan. "Never before have I returned a life to the land of the living, but never before have I met a woman like you. Take your husband and live with him happily."

You have a dream that suggests that Death will be paying you a visit tomorrow. Time is short. Devise a scheme, a story, a stall ... *anything* to convince the Grim Reaper that your time isn't up yet. With a partner play the scene for the class.

Activities

1. Assume that you have been given the choice of the kind of death you can have, the moon or the banana. Indicate your decision in the form of a petition or a prayer. Give reasons for your choice of one over the other.

2. The photograph of the Steele women suggests that continuity of life from generation to generation is the way immortality is reached on earth. Research the history of a famous family and report to the class how the family achieved "immortality" on earth. You may wish to consider the following families:

Kennedy
Rockefeller
Ford
Windsor
Hanover
Plantagenet
Hapsburg
Bourbon

Rothschild
Medici
Krupp
du Pont
Bach
Breughel
Redgrave
Brontë

3. Prepare a production of *On Borrowed Time* to be performed before the class. Use as many props as possible to set the stage (for example, a step ladder for the apple tree). Pay particular attention to stage directions and realistic portrayals of the characters.

7. While Mr. Brink was trapped in the apple tree, no one in the entire world died. Imagine the consequences of a world without death. Draw up a petition addressed to Gramps, stating why you believe Mr. Brink should either be freed or be kept as a prisoner in the tree.

4. Assume that after the first scene of *On Borrowed Time* Demetria succeeded in bringing Gramps into court for a sanity hearing. As Gramps' lawyer or Demetria's lawyer, prepare your case by pointing to evidence that is revealed in the play. Act out the courtroom scene before the class.

5. If Demetria had invited a newspaper reporter along with the doctor and the lawyer to witness Gramps' talking to Mr. Brink, how would the reporter have written his article for the local newspaper? Write his article, beginning with an eye-catching headline.

6. Gramps and Pud die and go off into eternity with Mr. Brink. Immediately Gramps hears the voice of his dead wife, Granny, whom he loves dearly, but who always scolded him for swearing. Write the conversation which Granny, Gramps, and Pud have at their reunion, in which Gramps and Pud try to explain all that has happened with Mr. Brink and Demetria since Granny died.

8. "Because I Could Not Stop for Death" can be interpreted as the dead person's description of her own funeral procession as the hearse takes her body to the cemetery. Write your own poem, describing what you might feel and see during your own funeral.

9. Adapt "Savitri and Death" into a play for children. Write the dialogue and stage directions and create your own props. You might consider doing a puppet show or a shadow play. Put your play on for a group of elementary school children.

10. Write a sequel to "Savitri and Death," in which Death comes to claim Savitri and her husband after many years of happy married life. How do you think Savitri would treat Yama at this second meeting? Would she give in or try to trick him further?

11. Savitri outwitted Death, whereas Death outwitted Gramps. Write a letter of advice which Savitri might have sent to Gramps while Mr. Brink was still trapped up in the tree. Exchange letters with a classmate and

Widespread famine will almost surely be an important check for our population epidemic, although thermo-nuclear war and the development of a virulant mutant virus are also possibilities. Each year an additional 70 million mouths must be fed. And each year, in spite of agricultural advances such as new high-yielding strains of rice and other grains, the amount of food per person drops.

Connecticut Conservation Association

8
Checks
and Balances

Lemmings are small, mouselike animals that live in Norway and Sweden. They breed in great numbers and, when their population becomes so great that their food supply becomes scarce, they migrate by the millions across the countryside and eat every bit of vegetation in their paths. On their journey, a disease known as lemming fever breaks out and kills many of them. Predators kill many more. Other creatures, including human beings, join in the destruction of lemmings by stamping their bodies under foot. This strange occurrence in the animal world would not make lemmings especially noteworthy were it not that once lemmings begin their migrations they never stop until they are dead. They continue their destructive journey until they reach the sea. By the millions they dive into the water, swim as far as they can, and drown. Nature's enforcement of its checks and balances on the lemming population would seem to destroy the entire species, yet every few years the process begins again.

It appears that humankind too cannot escape nature's checks and balances. With a small group of classmates, draw up a list of some of the natural and manmade checks and balances on the human population. On the blackboard record each group's findings and list them in order of the most destructive to the least destructive toward human life.

Be fruitful and multiply, and fill the
earth and subdue it; and have
dominion over the fish of the sea and
over the birds of the air and over every
living thing that moves upon the earth.

Genesis 1:28

A hundred years ago this summer, the
descendants of Richard Rich, who had
come to Cape Cod from England in 1650,
gathered for a reunion in Truro, Mass.
Most of the thousand who were there
sat with their family coat of arms for a
picture on a hillside. In 1965, the Rich
family again started holding reunions.
About 200 showed up at Cape Cod this
year to dedicate a plaque, have a clam-
bake and sit for another family picture.

A Dubliner himself, Jonathan Swift was deeply concerned with the problem of poverty and hunger in Ireland. Intentionally using outrageous and absurd reasoning for its shock value, Swift wrote his "modest proposal" in 1729 to draw England's attention to the problems of the Irish people who were being exploited by greedy British absentee landlords. What did Swift propose so modestly?

FROM A Modest Proposal

Jonathan Swift

I shall now therefore humbly propose my own thoughts, which I hope will not be liable to the least objection.

I have been assured by a very knowing American of my acquaintance in London, that a young healthy child well nursed is at a year old a most delicious, nourishing, and wholesome food, whether stewed, roasted, baked, or boiled, and I make no doubt that it will equally serve in a fricassee or a ragout.

I do therefore humbly offer it to public consideration that of the hundred and twenty thousand children already computed, twenty thousand may be reserved for breed, whereof only one fourth part to be males, which is more than we allow to sheep, black cattle, or swine; and my reason is that these children are seldom the fruits of marriage, a circumstance not much regarded by our savages. Therefore one male will be sufficient to serve four females. That the remaining hundred thousand may at a year old be offered in sale to the persons of quality and fortune through the kingdom, always advising the mother to let them suck plentifully in the last month, so as to render them plump and fat for a good table. A child will make two dishes at an entertainment for friends, and when the family dines alone, the fore or hind quarter will make a reasonable dish, and seasoned with a little pepper or salt will be very good boiled on the fourth day, especially in winter.

I have reckoned, upon a medium, that a child just born will weigh 12 pounds, and in a solar year if tolerably nursed will increase to 28 pounds.

I grant this food will be somewhat dear, and therefore very proper for landlords, who, as they have already devoured most of the parents, seem to have the best title to the children. . . .

I have already computed the charge of nursing a beggar's child (in which list I reckon all cottagers, labourers, and four-fifths of the farmers) to be about two shillings *per annum,* rags included,

Famine Spreads Through Africa

Food Prices Rise

Corn Crop Fails

Drought Strikes Midwest

Farmers Pessimistic

and I believe no gentleman would repine[1] to give ten shillings for the carcass of a good fat child, which, as I have said, will make four dishes of excellent nutritive meat, when he has only some particular friend or his own family to dine with him. Thus the squire will learn to be a good landlord, and grow popular among his tenants, the mother will have eight shillings net profit, and be fit for work till she produces another child.

Those who are more thrifty (as I must confess the times require) may flay the carcass; the skin of which, artificially dressed, will make admirable gloves for ladies, and summer boots for fine gentlemen.

As to our city of Dublin, shambles[2]

may be appointed for this purpose in the most convenient parts of it, and butchers we may be assured will not be wanting, although I rather recommend buying the children alive, and dressing them hot from the knife, as we do roasting pigs.

Swift hoped that people reading his satirical proposal would be so shocked and outraged as to offer serious proposals of their own. Assume that Swift's proposal was printed in a London newspaper in 1729 and that most of the people who read it did not see the satire but took it literally. Write a letter to the editor of the newspaper, explaining what you think Swift really intended to say. Quote phrases from the proposal that you think reveal Swift's true intentions.

---

[1] complain

[2] slaughterhouses

Satire draws our attention to problems and flaws in human nature by magnifying them all out of proportion. "A Bad Day for Sales" is a science fiction story about a robot salesman that blindly goes about peddling its wares in New York City's Times Square although most of its customers are lying dead in the streets.

A Bad Day for Sales

Fritz Leiber

The big bright doors parted with a *whoosh* and Robie glided suavely onto Times Square. The crowd that had been watching the fifty-foot tall clothing-ad girl get dressed, or reading the latest news about the Hot Truce scrawl itself in yard-high script, hurried to look.

Robie was still a novelty. Robie was fun. For a little while yet he could steal the show.

But the attention did not make Robie proud. He had no more vanity than the pink plastic giantess, and she did not even flicker her blue mechanical eyes.

Robie radared the crowd, found that it surrounded him solidly, and stopped. With a calculated mysteriousness, he said nothing.

"Say, ma, he doesn't look like a robot at all. He looks sort of like a turtle."

Which was not completely inaccurate. The lower part of Robie's body was a metal hemisphere hemmed with sponge rubber and not quite touching the sidewalk. The upper was a metal box with black holes in it. The box could swivel and duck.

A chromium-bright hoopskirt with a turret on top.

"Reminds me too much of the Little Joe Baratanks," a veteran of the Persian War muttered, and rapidly rolled himself away on wheels rather like Robie's.

His departure made it easier for some of those who knew about Robie to open a path in the crowd. Robie headed straight for the gap. The crowd whooped.

Robie glided very slowly down the path, deftly jogging aside whenever he got too close to ankles in skylon or sock-assins. The rubber buffer on his hoopskirt was merely an added safeguard.

The boy who had called Robie a turtle jumped in the middle of the path and stood his ground, grinning foxily.

Robie stopped two feet short of him. The turret ducked. The crowd got quiet.

"Hello, youngster," Robie said in a voice that was smooth as that of a TV star, and was in fact a recording of one.

The boy stopped smiling. "Hello," he whispered.

"How old are you?" Robie asked.

"Nine. No, eight."

109

"That's nice," Robie observed. A metal arm shot down from his neck, stopped just short of the boy. The boy jerked back.

"For you," Robie said gently.

The boy gingerly took the red polly-lop from the neatly-fashioned blunt metal claws. A gray-haired woman whose son was a paraplegic hurried on.

After a suitable pause Robie continued, "And how about a nice refreshing drink of Poppy Pop to go with your polly-lop?" The boy lifted his eyes but didn't stop licking the candy. Robie wiggled his claws ever so slightly. "Just give me a quarter and within five seconds—"

A little girl wriggled out of the forest of legs. "Give me a polly-lop too, Robie," she demanded.

"Rita, come back here," a woman in the third rank of the crowd called angrily.

Robie scanned the newcomer gravely. His reference silhouettes were not good enough to let him distinguish the sex of children, so he merely repeated, "Hello youngster."

"Rita!"

"Give me a polly-lop!"

Disregarding both remarks, for a good salesman is single-minded and does not waste bait, Robie said winningly, "I'll bet you read *Junior Space Killers.* Now I have here—"

"Uh-hhh, I'm a girl. *He* got a polly-lop."

At the word "girl" Robie broke off. Rather ponderously he said, "Then—" After another pause he continued, "I'll bet you read *Gee-Gee Jones, Space Stripper.* Now I have here the latest issue of that thrilling comic, not yet in the stationary vending machines. Just give me fifty cents and within five—"

"Please let me through. I'm her mother."

A young woman in the front rank drawled over her powder-sprayed shoulder, "I'll get her for you," and slithered out on six-inch platforms. "Run away, children," she said nonchalantly and lifting her arms behind her head, pirouetted slowly before Robie to show how much she did for her bolero half-jacket and her form-fitting slacks that melted into skylon just above the knees. The little girl glared at her. She ended the pirouette in profile.

At this age-level Robie's reference silhouettes permitted him to distinguish sex, though with occasional amusing and embarrassing miscalls. He whistled admiringly. The crowd cheered.

Someone remarked critically to his friend. "It would go better if he was built more like a real robot. You know, like a man."

The friend shook his head. "This way it's subtler."

No one in the crowd was watching the newscript overhead as it scribbled, "Ice Pack for Hot Truce? Vanadin hints Russ may yield on Pakistan."

Robie was saying, ". . . in the savage new glamor-tint we have christened Mars Blood, complete with spray applicator and fit-all fingerstalls that mask each finger completely except for the nail. Just give me five dollars—uncrumpled bills may be fed into the revolving rollers you see beside my arm—and within five seconds,—"

"No thanks, Robie," the young woman yawned.

"Remember," Robie persisted, "for three more weeks seductivising Mars Blood will be unobtainable from any other robot or human vendor."

"No thanks."

Robie scanned the crowed resourcefully. "Is there any gentleman here . . ."

he began just as a woman elbowed her way through the front rank.

"I told you to come back!" she snarled at the little girl.

"But I didn't get my polly-lop!"

". . . who would care to . . ."

"Rita!"

"Robie cheated. Ow!"

Meanwhile the young woman in the half-bolero had scanned the nearby gentlemen on her own. Deciding that there was less than a fifty per cent chance of any of them accepting the proposition Robie seemed about to make, she took advantage of the scuffle to slither gracefully back into the ranks. Once again the path was clear before Robie.

He paused, however, for a brief recapitulation of the more magical properties of Mars Blood, including a telling phrase about "the passionate claws of a Martian sunrise."

But no one bought. It wasn't quite time yet. Soon enough silver coins would be clinking, bills going through the rollers faster than laundry, and five hundred people struggling for the privilege of having their money taken away from them by America's only genuine mobile sales-robot.

But now was too soon. There were still some tricks that Robie did free, and one certainly should enjoy those before starting the more expensive fun.

So Robie moved on until he reached the curb. The variation in level was instantly sensed by his under-scanners. He stopped. His head began to swivel. The crowd watched in eager silence. This was Robie's best trick.

Robie's head stopped swiveling. His scanners had found the traffic light. It was green. Robie edged forward. But then it turned red. Robie stopped again, still on the curb. The crowd softly *ahhed* its delight.

Oh, it was wonderful to be alive and watching Robie on such a wonderful day. Alive and amused in the fresh, weather-controlled air between the lines of bright skyscrapers with their winking windows and under a sky so blue you could almost call it dark.

(But way, way up, where the crowd could not see, the sky was darker still. Purple-dark, with stars showing. And in that purple-dark, a silver-green something, the color of a bud, plunged downward at better than three miles a second. The silver-green was a paint that foiled radar.)

Robie was saying, "While we wait for the light there's time for you youngsters to enjoy a nice refreshing Poppy Pop. Or for you adults—only those over five feet are eligible to buy—to enjoy an exciting Poppy Pop fizz. Just give me a quarter or—I'm licenced to dispense intoxicating liquors—in the case of adults one dollar and a quarter and within five seconds . . .

But that was not cutting it quite fine enough. Just three seconds later the silver-green bud bloomed above Manhattan into a globular orange flower. The skyscrapers grew brighter and brighter still, the brightness of the inside of the sun. The windows winked white fire.

The crowd around Robie bloomed too. Their clothes puffed into petals of flame. Their heads of hair were torches.

The orange flower grew, stem and blossom. The blast came. The winking windows shattered tier by tier, became black holes. The walls bent, rocked, cracked. A stony dandruff dribbled from their cornices. The flaming flowers on the sidewalk were all leveled at once. Robie was shoved ten feet. His metal hoopskirt dimpled, regained its shape.

The blast ended. The orange flower, grown vast, vanished overhead on its huge, magic beanstalk. It grew dark and very still. The cornice-dandruff pattered down. A few small fragments rebounded from the metal hoopskirt.

Robie made some small, uncertain movements, as if feeling for broken bones. He was hunting for the traffic light, but it no longer shone, red or green.

He slowly scanned a full circle. There was nothing anywhere to interest his reference silhouettes. Yet whenever he tried to move, his under-scanners warned him of low obstructions. It was very puzzling.

The silence was disturbed by moans and a crackling sound, faint at first as the scampering of rats.

A seared man, his charred clothes fuming where the blast had blown out the fire, rose from the curb. Robie scanned him.

"Good day, sir," Robie said. "Would you care for a smoke? A truly cool smoke? Now I have here a yet-unmarketed brand . . ."

But the customer had run away, screaming, and Robie never ran after customers, though he could follow them at a medium brisk roll. He worked his way along the curb where the man had sprawled, carefully keeping his distance from the low obstructions, some of which writhed now and then, forcing him to jog. Shortly he reached a fire hydrant. He scanned it. His electronic vision, though it still worked, had been somewhat blurred by the blast.

"Hello, youngster," Robie said. Then, after a long pause, "Cat got your tongue? Well, I've got a little present for you. A nice, lovely polly-lop." His metal arm snaked down.

"Take it, youngster," he said after another pause. "It's for you. Don't be afraid."

His attention was distracted by other customers, who began to rise up oddly here and there, twisting forms that confused his reference silhouettes and would not stay to be scanned properly. One cried, "Water," but no quarter clinked in Robie's claws when he caught the word and suggested, "How about a nice refreshing drink of Poppy Pop?"

The rat-crackling of the flames had become a jungle muttering. The blind windows began to wink fire again.

A little girl marched up, stepping neatly over arms and legs she did not look at. A white dress and the once taller bodies around her had shielded her from the brilliance and the blast. Her eyes were fixed on Robie. In them was the same imperious confidence, though none of the delight, with which she had watched him earlier.

"Help me, Robie," she said. "I want my mother."

"Hello, youngster," Robie said. "What would you like? Comics? Candy?"

"Where is she, Robie? Take me to her."

"Balloons? Would you like to watch me blow up a balloon?"

The little girl began to cry. The sound triggered off another of Robie's novelty circuits.

"Is something wrong?" he asked. "Are you in trouble? Are you lost?"

"Yes, Robie. Take me to my mother."

"Stay right here," Robie said reassuringly, "and don't be frightened. I will call a policeman." He whistled shrilly, twice.

Time passed. Robie whistled again. The windows flared and roared. The little girl begged, "Take me away, Robie," and jumped onto a little step in his hoopskirt.

"Give me a dime," Robie said. The little girl found one in her pocket and put it in his claws.

"Your weight," Robie said, "is fifty-four and one-half pounds, exactly."

"Have you seen my daughter, have you seen her?" a woman was crying somewhere. "I left her watching that thing while I stepped inside—Rita!"

"Robie helped me," the little girl was telling her moments later. "He knew I was lost. He even called a policeman, but he didn't come. He weighed me too. Didn't you Robie?"

But Robie had gone off to peddle Poppy Pop to the members of a rescue squad which had just come around the corner, more robot-like than he in their fireproof clothing.

"A Bad Day for Sales" attacks the "plasticized" commercialism of our society. Review the story and list all the different products that Robie tries to sell. Note the sales pitch that Robie uses for each product. List some additional products that you think Robie may be programmed to sell. Write Robie's sales pitch for each product.

Plague

Great was the stench of the dead. After
our fathers and grandfathers succumbed,
half of the people fled to the fields.
The dogs and the vultures devoured the
bodies. The mortality was terrible.
Your grandfathers died, and with them
died the son of the king and his brothers
and kinsmen. So it was that we became
orphans, O my sons! So we became when
we were young. All of us were thus.
We were born to die!

Cakchiquel

The Cakchiquel peoples of Guatemala are not the only people in recorded history who have been devastated by plague or other epidemics. Between 1347 and 1351, Europe lost half its population through a plague called the Black Death: it is estimated that 75,000,000 people died. Between April and November of 1918, over 21,000,000 people died in a worldwide epidemic of influenza. In today's world of vaccines and antibiotics, we tend to forget these checks and balances that nature can unleash from time to time. Who would think today that the childhood disease of measles once wiped out half the native population of Hawaii? James A. Michener's fictional account vividly describes the spread of this dread epidemic.

The Scourge of the Pacific

James A. Michener

... Lahaina was about to be visited by a pestilence known as the scourge of the Pacific. On earlier trips to Hawaii this dreadful plague had wiped out more than half the population, and now it stood poised in the fo'c's'l of a whaler resting in Lahaina Roads, prepared to strike once more with demonic force, killing, laying waste, destroying an already doomed population. It was the worst disease of the Pacific: measles.

This time it started innocently by jumping from the diseased whaler and into the mission home, where immunities built up during a hundred generations in England and Massachusetts confined the disease to a trivial childhood sickness. Jerusha, inspecting her son Micah's chest one morning, found the customary red rash. "Have you a sore throat?" she asked, and when Micah said yes, she informed Abner, "I'm afraid our son has the measles."

Abner groaned and said, "I suppose Lucy and David and Esther are bound to catch it in turn," and he took down his medical books to see what he should do for the worrisome fever. Medication was simple and the routine not burdensome, so he said, "We'll plan for three weeks of keeping the children indoors." But it occurred to him that it might be prudent to see if John Whipple had any medicine for reducing the fever more quickly, and so he stopped casually by J & W's to report, "Worse luck! Micah seems to have the measles and I suppose . . ."

Whipple dropped his pen and cried, "Did you say measles?"

"Well, spots on his chest."

"Oh, my God!" Whipple mumbled, grabbing his bag and rushing to the mission house. With trembling fingers he inspected the sick boy and Jerusha saw that the doctor was perspiring.

"Are measles so dangerous?" she asked with apprehension.

"Not for him," Whipple replied. He

116

We are vanishing from the earth, yet I cannot think we are useless or Usen [Apache word for God] would not have created us. . . .

Geronimo

then led the parents into the front room and asked in a whisper, "Have you been in contact with any Hawaiians since Micah became ill?"

"No," Abner reflected. "I walked down to your store."

"Thank God," Whipple gasped, washing his hands carefully. "Abner, we have only a slight chance of keeping this dreadful disease away from the Hawaiians, but I want your entire family to stay in this house for three weeks. See nobody."

Jerusha challenged him directly: "Brother John, is it indeed the measles?"

"It is," he replied, "and I would to God it were anything else. We had better prepare ourselves, for there may be sad days ahead." Then, awed by the gravity of the threat, he asked impulsively, "Abner, would you please say a prayer for all of us . . . for Lahaina? Keep the pestilence from this town." And they knelt while Abner prayed.

But men from the infected whaler had moved freely through the community, and on the next morning Dr. Whipple happened to look out of his door to see a native man, naked, digging himself a shallow grave beside the ocean, where cool water could seep in and fill the sandy rectangle. Rushing to the reef, Whipple called, "Kekuana, what are you doing?" And the Hawaiian, shivering

fearfully, replied, "I am burning to death and the water will cool me." At this Dr. Whipple said sternly, "Go back to your home, Kekuana, and wrap yourself in tapa. Sweat this illness out or you will surely die." But the man argued, "You do not know how terrible the burning fire is," and he sank himself in the salt water and within the day he died.

Now all along the beach Hawaiians, spotted with measles, dug themselves holes in the cool wet sand, and in spite of anything Dr. Whipple could tell them, crawled into the comforting waters and died. The cool irrigation ditches and taro patches were filled with corpses. Through the miserable huts of the town the pestilence swept like fire, burning its victims with racking fevers that could not be endured. Dr. Whipple organized his wife, the Hales and the Janderses into a medical team that worked for three weeks, arguing, consoling and burying. Once Abner cried in frustration, "John, why do these stubborn people insist upon plunging into the surf when they know it kills them?" And Whipple replied in exhaustion, "We are misled because we call the fever measles. In these unprotected people it is something much worse. Abner, you have never known such a fever."

Nevertheless, the little missionary pleaded with his patients, "If you go into the water, you will die."

"I want to die, Makua Hale," they replied.

Write the public notice which Dr. Whipple might have tacked on a tree in the village center, warning the Hawaiians of the symptoms and dangers of measles and telling what to do and what not to do at the onset of fever.

Like war, pollution is a manmade problem which threatens not only human life but all life. Probably no book has drawn so much public attention to the problem of pollution as Rachel Carson's *The Silent Spring,* from which "A Fable for Tomorrow" comes.

A Fable for Tomorrow

Rachel Carson

There was once a town in the heart of America where all life seemed to live in harmony with its surroundings. The town lay in the midst of a checkerboard of prosperous farms, with fields of grain and hillsides of orchards where, in spring, white clouds of bloom drifted above the green fields. In autumn, oak and maple and birch set up a blaze of color that flamed and flickered across a backdrop of pines. Then foxes barked in the hills and deer silently crossed the fields, half hidden in the mists of the fall mornings.

Along the roads, laurel, viburnum and alder, great ferns and wildflowers delighted the traveler's eye through much of the year. Even in winter the roadsides were places of beauty, where countless birds came to feed on the berries and on the seed heads of the dried weeds rising above the snow. The countryside was, in fact, famous for the abundance and variety of its bird life, and when the flood of migrants was pouring through in spring and fall people traveled from great distances to observe them. Others came to fish the streams which flowed clear and cold out of the hills and contained shady pools where trout lay. So it had been

from the days many years ago when the first settlers raised their houses, sank their wells, and built their barns.

Then a strange blight crept over the area and everything began to change. Some evil spell had settled on the community: mysterious maladies swept the flocks of chickens; the cattle and sheep sickened and died. Everywhere was a shadow of death. The farmers spoke of much illness among their families. In the town the doctors had become more and more puzzled by new kinds of sickness appearing among their patients. There had been several sudden and unexplained deaths, not only among adults but even among children, who would be stricken suddenly while at play and die within a few hours.

There was a strange stillness. The birds, for example—where had they gone? Many people spoke of them, puzzled and disturbed. The feeding stations in the backyards were deserted. The few birds seen anywhere were moribund; they trembled violently and could not fly. It was a spring without voices. On the mornings that had once throbbed with the dawn chorus of robins, catbirds, doves, jays,

wrens, and scores of other bird voices there was now no sound; only silence lay over the fields and woods and marsh.

On the farms the hens brooded, but no chicks hatched. The farmers complained that they were unable to raise any pigs—the litters were small and the young survived only a few days. The apple trees were coming into bloom but no bees droned among the blossoms, so there was no pollination and there would be no fruit.

The roadsides, once so attractive, were now lined with browned and withered vegetation as though swept by fire. These, too, were silent, deserted by all living things. Even the streams were now lifeless. Anglers no longer visited them, for all the fish had died.

In the gutters under the eaves and between the shingles of the roofs, a white granular powder still showed a few patches; some weeks before it had fallen like snow upon the roofs and the lawns, the fields and streams.

No witchcraft, no enemy action had silenced the rebirth of new life in this stricken world. The people had done it themselves.

This town does not actually exist, but it might easily have a thousand counterparts in America or elsewhere in the world. I know of no community that has experienced all the misfortunes I describe. Yet every one of these disasters has actually happened somewhere, and many real communities have already suffered a substantial number of them. A grim specter has crept upon us almost unnoticed, and this imagined tragedy may easily become a stark reality as we all shall know.

What has already silenced the voices of spring in countless towns in America?

Rachel Carson's choice of words helps create a vivid picture of the town and the overall fablelike tone of her writing. For example, in the first paragraph she uses the words *blaze, flamed,* and *flickered* to describe autumn. Newspaper articles seldom use this type of language, concentrating instead on words that relay the bare facts. Rewrite "A Fable for Tomorrow" as a newspaper article. Give it a new title and report only the facts.

Science and determination have succeeded in eliminating many of the checks and balances on human life. For example, doctors have eliminated smallpox epidemics that once claimed thousands of lives every year. Seismologists in China were able to predict a coming earthquake early enough so that there was time to evacuate the area. Engineers have built irrigation systems, and botanists have developed high-yield crops, thus eliminating famine in some parts of the world. Yet are we still headed for self-destruction like the lemmings? Some scientists urge that we change our way of life before it is too late. Others rely on human ingenuity to save us from any forthcoming disaster.

The two articles that follow present opposing views in this continuing public debate.

The Worst Is Yet to Be?

The furnaces of Pittsburgh are cold; the assembly lines of Detroit are still. In Los Angeles, a few gaunt survivors of a plague desperately till freeway center strips, backyards and outlying fields, hoping to raise a subsistence crop. London's offices are dark, its docks deserted. In the farm lands of the Ukraine, abandoned tractors litter the fields: there is no fuel for them. The waters of the Rhine, Nile and Yellow rivers reek with pollutants.

Fantastic? No, only grim inevitability if society continues its present dedication to growth and "progress." At least that is the vision conjured by an elaborate study entitled *The Limits to Growth.* Its sponsors are no latter-day Jeremiahs, but the 70 eminently respectable members of the prestigious Club of Rome. . . .

The club was founded by Peccei back in 1968 with the avowed purpose of exploring the large issues confronting society. "We needed something to make mankind's predicament more visible, more easy to grasp," says Peccei. To that end, the Volkswagen Foundation granted the club $250,000 in 1970. Peccei turned to an international team of scientists led by M.I.T. Computer Expert Dennis Meadows and told them to study the most basic issue of all—survival.

The question Meadows had to answer was: How long can population and industrialization continue to grow on this finite planet? Unlike the doomsday ecologists who predict that man will drown in pollution or starve because of overpopulation, Meadows' system concludes that the depletion of nonrenewable resources will probably cause the end of the civilization enjoyed by today's contented consumer.

The Meadows team offers a possible cure for man's dilemma—an all-out effort to end exponential growth, starting by 1975. Population should be stabilized by equalizing the birth and death rates. To halt industrial growth, investment in new, nonpolluting plants must not exceed the retirement of old facilities. A series of fundamental shifts in behavioral patterns must take place. Instead of yearning for material goods, people must learn to prefer services, like education or recreation.

Time, January 24, 1972

A COLLISION COURSE WITH DOOMSDAY?

Walter B. Wriston

Anyone in our society whose eyesight and hearing are not totally impaired is likely to believe that we are on a collision course with Doomsday.

The compulsion[1] of the media to turn every scrap of bad news into a full-blown crisis distorts our perspective. It neglects to remind us that troubles may be news, but they are by no means new. This negative emphasis ignores the decisive role of human ingenuity in a free society. One of our distinguished historians, Barbara Tuchman, recently put it this way: "The doomsayers work by extrapolation; they take a trend and extend it, forgetting that the doom factor, sooner or later, generates a coping mechanism.... You cannot extrapolate any series in which the human element intrudes; history, that is the human narrative, never follows and will always fool, the scientific curve." How right is her insight; alarmists' curves frequently are based upon downward trends. As early as the sixth chapter of Genesis some believed the world was headed downhill. The doomsayers were already looking back upon better times: "There were giants in the earth in those days."

Prophets of doom have a second weakness. They fail to appreciate man's inherent ability to adjust and innovate. The British economist Thomas Malthus predicted in 1798 that the imbalance between population growth and food production would cause the world to starve to death. The doomsayers called it Malthus' iron law. As time has proved, it was neither iron nor law. Like many of our current crop of transient[2] experts, Malthus fell into the oldest trap of all in the prognostication[3] game. He underestimated everyone's intelligence but his own; he was incapable of imagining that out of the Industrial Revolution would come reapers, threshers, combines and tractors. He did not foresee the era of cheap energy. Nor did he envision chemicals and fertilizers creating such abundance that foolish governments would pay farmers *not* to cultivate the soil.

A third fault accounts for the inability of the doomsayers accurately to predict what will happen. They cling to the belief that there are accepted absolutes in a world of rapidly changing value systems. As the French poet, Paul Valery, put it, we often tend to be marching backward into the future.

---

[1] an irresistible, repeated, irrational impulse to perform some act

[2] temporary

[3] prediction

Has Mr. Wriston successfully answered the pessimistic predictions of the Club of Rome? Write down each side's position in a sentence or two. Then list the arguments mentioned in each article that are used to support these positions. Finally, write a short statement explaining why you would support one side over the other.

The North American Indians had an undying respect for nature and tried to live in harmony with the world around them. Understandably, they became bewildered and angered when they saw the White man changing the order of things.

# of Indian Existence | T. C. McLuhan

FROM **Touch the Earth: A Self-Portrait**

Once we were happy in our own country and we were seldom hungry, for then the two-leggeds and the four-leggeds lived together like relatives, and there was plenty for them and for us. But the Wasichus came, and they have made little islands for us and other little islands for the four-leggeds, and always these islands are becoming smaller, for around them surges the gnawing flood of the Wasichu; and it is dirty with lies and greed.

I can remember when the bison were so many that they could not be counted, but more and more Wasichus came to kill them until there were only heaps of bones scattered where they used to be. The Wasichus did not kill them to eat; they killed them for the metal that makes them crazy, and they took only the hides to sell. Sometimes they did not even take the hides, only the tongues; and I have heard that fire-boats came down the Missouri River loaded with dried bison tongues. Sometimes they did not even take the tongues; they just killed and killed because they liked to do that.

Black Elk, *Sioux Chief*

The White people never cared for land or deer or bear. When we Indians kill meat, we eat it all up. When we dig roots we make little holes. When we build houses, we make little holes. When we burn grass for grasshoppers, we don't ruin things. We shake down acorns and pinenuts. We don't chop down the trees. We only use dead wood. But the White people plow up the ground, pull down the trees, kill everything. The tree says, "Don't. I am sore. Don't hurt me." But they chop it down and cut it up. The spirit of the land hates them. They blast out trees and stir it up to its depths. They saw up the trees. That hurts them. The Indians never hurt anything, but the White people destroy all. They blast rocks and scatter them on the ground. The rock says, "Don't. You are hurting me." But the White people pay no attention. When the Indians use rocks, they take little round ones for their cooking. . . . Everywhere the White man has touched the earth, it is sore.

An old holy Wintu woman of California

Assuming the identity of either Black Elk or the Wintu woman, write a telegram to the Bureau of Indian Affairs, protesting the destruction of the natural resources necessary for Indian life.

1. Compare population figures in a current almanac with those in older editions. Consider your town, city, state, or other place of special interest to you. Prepare a graph to illustrate your findings.

Activities

2. Jonathan Swift's solution to the economic problems of Ireland is deliberately shocking; however, we may be forced to consider extreme measures in the future if our resources and ingenuity cannot keep pace with our population's needs. With a group of classmates, think of several solutions to this potential problem. List all of your group's ideas, no matter how impossible they may sound. Compare your group's ideas with those of the other groups. Draw up one final list of those solutions judged best by the class. Follow with a class discussion exploring the arguments in opposition to population control.

3. Television comedians often satirize commercial advertisements. With a group of classmates, select some of the advertisements that regularly appear on television and prepare satirical reenactments of them to be performed before the class.

4. There are many famous pieces of literature dealing with plagues and epidemics. Samuel Pepys' *Diary*, written in 1665, gives a day-to-day account of the London plague in the months from June 15 to November 15. The introduction to "Day the First" in Boccaccio's *Decameron* tells of the Black Death which swept across medieval Europe. Edgar Allan Poe's "The Masque of the Red Death" is a short story about a plague. Albert Camus wrote a novel called *The Plague*—a reading of Part I, chapter 2 will provide a sample. Also, midway through chapter 4 of James A. Michener's *Hawaii* there is a section about leprosy. Select one of these pieces for outside reading and prepare an oral report on it.

5. "A Fable for Tomorrow" describes the effects of several kinds of pollution. Using materials from the school library, write a report about one type of pollution and its effect on health and the environment.

6. List the images which Rachel Carson uses to describe either a beautiful world or a blighted world. By making a few changes for the sake of rhythm, turn your list into a free verse poem.

7. Write a letter to either The Club of Rome ("The Worst Is Yet to Be," p. 120) or to Walter Wriston ("A Collision Course with Doomsday?", p. 121) in reaction to their points of view.

8. Prepare an oral report on the history and culture of one American Indian tribe.

9. Interview an old resident of your neighborhood and ask him or her to tell you about the changes that have taken place as a result of increased population pressures. Report what you find to the class.

10. Go for a short walk and count something in your environment. Are there too many? or too few? Report what you counted and what you learned from that count to the rest of the class.

9
The End of the World

"Nothing lasts forever" is a familiar generalization which seems true for most things. Does this include the world too? If so, how much longer will the world last and how will it finally come to an end?

With a group of classmates, discuss all the ways in which the world could end and make a list of them. Compare your list with those of the other groups and record one combined list on the blackboard. Next, take a vote to determine which of the causes listed on the blackboard seem to the class most likely to end the world. Finally, conduct a survey of the class to determine when the end of the world may occur.

This is the way the world ends
This is the way the world ends
This is the way the world ends
Not with a bang but a whimper.

T. S. Eliot, "The Hollow Men"

If the world were to end suddenly in
the near future, where do you think you
would be at the time? Imagine yourself
under the big top at a three-ring circus.

The End of the World

Archibald MacLeish

Quite unexpectedly as Vasserot
The armless ambidextrian was lighting
A match between his great and second toe
And Ralph the lion was engaged in biting
The neck of Madame Sossman while the drum
Pointed, and Teeny was about to cough
In waltz-time swinging Jocko by the thumb—
Quite unexpectedly the top blew off:

And there, there overhead, there, there, hung over
Those thousands of white faces, those dazed eyes,
There in the starless dark the poise, the hover,
There with vast wings across the canceled skies,
There in the sudden blackness the black pall
Of nothing, nothing, nothing—nothing at all.

Write your own description of the
end of the world. In the first part
describe the place where you are
just before the end of the world,
and in the second part describe
exactly what happens. You might
want to use a poetic form.

By observing the movement of stars
and galaxies, scientists can theorize
about how the universe will end.
According to John W. Clark, it is all a
matter of gravity and time.

The Big Bang Theory

John W. Clark

As the life of man has its season, so does the life of the universe. The universe
is observed to be expanding at a prodigious[1] rate. The galaxies and dust clouds
of which it is made are receding from one another at speeds up to that of light.
A gigantic explosion is in progress. Some eleven billion years ago the universe
was supposedly confined to a tiny space, formless, but possessing great potency,
great energy. In an instant, the fundamental physical constraints, like the
charge on the electron, were decided by chance; then the physical laws of our
universe took over and there was a tremendous explosion—the "big bang."
Eventually the energy of the explosion will be used up, and the expansion will
slow to a halt because of the gravitational attraction of all the pieces of matter for
one another. The universe will thereupon contract, ultimately down to the same
exceedingly tiny space in which it was born. The scenario[2] will then repeat,
with different fundamental constants. There will be a cyclic creation and
destruction of universes, all subtly different. Each cycle is believed to take
about eighty billion years, so there is no need to panic.

---

[1] enormous   [2] a script, as for a motion picture

**John W. Clark theorizes that the universe as we know
it will end in about 70 billion years—a long time away
indeed. Write a short description of what you imagine
the earth will be like as the end approaches.**

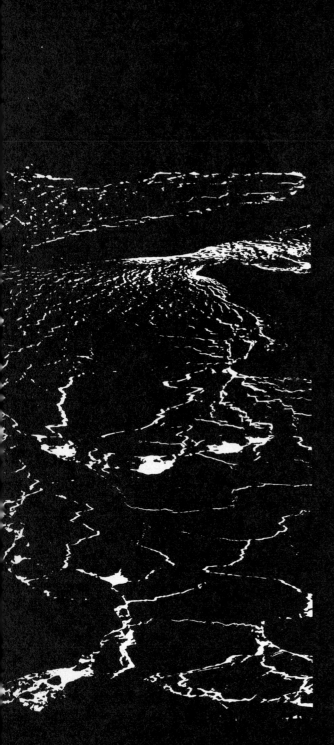

Writers of science fiction base their ideas on known scientific facts and theories. In *The Time Machine,* H. G. Wells described the end of the world with imaginative details that are still very close to some scientific theories. In the following excerpt, the narrator has used his amazing invention to travel more than 30 million years into the future. Green slime on rocks is the only indication of life in a cold, black, silent world; and then the traveler sees another sign of life.

FROM The Time Machine

H. G. Wells

"I looked about me to see if any traces of animal life remained. A certain indefinable apprehension still kept me in the saddle of the machine. But I saw nothing moving, in earth or sky or sea. The green slime on the rocks alone testified that life was not extinct. A shallow sand-bank had appeared in the sea and the water had receded from the beach. I fancied I saw some black object flopping about upon this bank, but it became motionless as I looked at it, and I judged that my eye had been deceived, and that the black object was merely a rock. The stars in the sky were intensely bright and seemed to me to twinkle very little.

"Suddenly I noticed that the circular westward outline of the sun had changed; that a concavity, a bay, had appeared in the curve. I saw this grow larger. For a minute perhaps I stared aghast at this blackness that was creeping over the day, and then I realized that an eclipse was beginning. Either the moon or the planet Mercury was passing across the sun's disk. Naturally, at first I took it to be the moon, but there is much to incline me to believe that what I really saw was the transit of an inner planet passing very near to the earth.

"The darkness grew apace; a cold wind began to blow in freshening gusts from the east, and the showering white flakes in the air increased in number. From the edge of the sea came a ripple and whisper. Beyond these lifeless sounds the world was silent. Silent? It would be hard to convey the stillness of it. All the sounds of man, the bleating of sheep, the cries of birds, the hum of insects, the stir that makes the background of our lives— all that was over. As the darkness thickened, the eddying flakes grew more abundant, dancing before my eyes; and the cold of the air more intense. At last, one by one, swiftly, one after the other, the white peaks of the distant hills vanished into blackness. The breeze rose to a moaning wind. I saw the black central shadow of the eclipse sweeping towards me. In another moment the pale stars alone were visible. All else was rayless obscurity. The sky was absolutely black.

"A horror of this great darkness came on me. The cold, that smote to my marrow, and the pain I felt in breathing, overcame me. I shivered, and a deadly nausea seized me. Then like a red-hot bow in the sky appeared the edge of the sun. I got off the machine to recover myself. I felt giddy and incapable of facing the return journey. As I stood sick and confused I saw again the moving thing upon the shoal—there was no mistake now that it was a moving thing—against

the red water of the sea. It was a round thing, the size of a football perhaps, or, it may be, bigger, and tentacles trailed down from it; it seemed black against the weltering blood-red water, and it was hopping fitfully about. Then I felt I was fainting. But a terrible dread of lying helpless in that remote and awful twilight sustained me while I clambered upon the saddle."

Compare the description in which you have written about the end of the world with this selection from *The Time Machine*. How are they different? Rewrite your original description as if you were the narrator of H. G. Wells' novel.

The sun is slowly burning out in
H. G. Wells' vision of the end of the
world, and human life has long vanished
from the face of the earth. In contrast,
Lord Byron's "dream" is very much like
Archibald MacLeish's poem: suddenly
all humanity is faced with darkness.

FROM Darkness

George Gordon, Lord Byron

I had a dream, which was not all a dream,
The bright sun was extinguish'd, and the stars
Did wander darkling in the eternal space,
Rayless, and pathless; and the icy earth
Swung blind and blackening in the moonless air
Morn came and went—and came, and brought no day,
And men forgot their passions in the dread
Of this their desolation: and all hearts
Were chill'd into a selfish prayer for light:

Imagine that you wake up one
morning and the sun is no longer
giving off light and heat. Write an
imaginary diary entry of your
thoughts and feelings. Include a
description of what happens in your
neighborhood when everyone realizes that the end of the world is
approaching.

According to the Bible, God destroyed everything on earth except the lives that were sheltered in Noah's Ark. Will a flood destroy the earth again? Or will it be fire and ice? Robert Frost's poem suggests that mankind will bring about its own destruction again, either through the fire of desire or through the ice of hate.

Fire and Ice

Robert Frost

Some say the world will end in fire,
Some say in ice.
From what I've tasted of desire
I hold with those who favor fire.
But if it had to perish twice,
I think I know enough of hate
To say that for destruction ice
Is also great
And would suffice.

Much of the meaning of Frost's poem relies on our associating fire and ice with the human emotions of desire and hate. Many phrases in our language make similar connections between apparently unconnectable ideas. Complete the following phrases with a suitable word from the list on the right. Then use each completed phrase in a sentence that makes its meaning clear.

1. in the heat of _____
2. a fiery _____
3. an icy _____
4. a cold _____
5. a warm _____
6. a cool _____
7. a hot _____

shoulder
reply
item
(an) argument
temper
personality
time
move
battle
stare
speech

Just as there are myths about the creation, there are myths about the end of the world. In Norse mythology, all is destroyed when the forces of evil rise up to wage war against the gods.

Ragnarokk, the Destiny of the Gods

Ingri and Edgar d' Aulaire

Then Odin[1] knew that Ragnarokk, the day of reckoning when the destiny of the gods would be decided, was fast approaching. Soon the Aesir[2] must face the forces of destruction and win over them, or be themselves destroyed.

There was no more kindness among gods or men since gentle Balder[3] had passed over to the gloomy realm of Hel[4]. Brother could no longer trust brother. In their lust for gold men stole from each other and killed each other, and bloody wars raged all over the earth. Odin and his Valkyries[5] rushed from battlefield to battlefield to gather as many heroes as they could to fight in the last battle. Even the vast hall of Valhalla[6] was getting crowded.

Thor[7] was as busy as his father, forever on the go, fighting jotuns[8] and trolls. For the monsters were getting bolder, drawing ever closer, pelting the world with snow and ice. Their frosty breath spread an icy fog over the earth, shutting out the warm rays of the sun.

And a winter came that lasted for three years. Deep snow covered the ground; nothing could sprout, nothing could grow. Men no longer fought for gold, but for food, and Hel's hall was filled to bursting with all those who had died of starvation.

[1] the mightiest of the gods, god of art, culture, war, and the dead

[2] the principal gods of Norse mythology as a group

[3] the god of light, peace, virtue, and wisdom, killed by the god of mischief

[4] the underworld to which the dead not killed in battle were sent

[5] the maidens of Odin who conduct the souls of heroes killed in battle to Valhalla and wait on them there

[6] the great hall where Odin receives and feasts with the souls of heroes fallen bravely in battle

[7] the god of thunder, war, and strength, and the son of Odin

[8] giants

Then, early one morning, long before daybreak, the golden cock of Asgard[9] stretched out his neck and crowed loudly. An answer came echoing up through the ground from the soot-black cock that perched on the roof of Hel's hall. The day of Ragnarokk had come.

The earth split open, all the way to the world of the dead, and all the bonds of the world broke with a twang. . . .

The din of the monsters was so loud that the vault of the sky split open. Through the crack burst Surt, ruler of Muspelheim, the world of fire. He swung his flaming sword, and it set fire to everything it touched as he rushed toward the rainbow bridge. Behind him surged his warriors, horde upon horde of fire demons, all set upon conquering Asgard. But when they stormed the shimmering bridge it broke and fell.

Surt and his warriors then made for the wide field of Vigrid, the greatest field in the world. One hundred miles long and one hundred miles wide, it was a proper battlefield for gods and giants. There the fire demons were joined by the hordes of trolls and jotuns, ghosts and monsters. In row upon row, they waited for the Aesir to come and give battle.

Led by Odin, the huge army of gods and heroes thundered up the field. Odin made straight for the gaping jaws of Fenris[10]. But before he could throw his spear down the wolf's horrible gullet, the monster lurched forward and swallowed him.

Thor could not come to his father's aid; he had his hands full fighting the Midgard's[11] Serpent. Time and again he threw his hammer at the hissing head, until at last the serpent gave up its breath and died. Thor lived only long enough to stagger nine steps backward. Then he fell to the ground, killed by the serpent's poisonous breath. . . .

Odin's vast army of heroes fought as long as there was a man standing, though jotuns and trolls pelted them with blocks of ice, with boulders, yes, even with mountains.

At last the battle ended. Most of the Aesir and all of Odin's warriors lay dead, and the sound of the goddesses weeping filled the world.

Then the two jotuns in wolf's clothing caught up with sun and moon and swallowed them.

The Aesir world was plunged into darkness, and Yggdrasil[12], the world tree, broke and fell. Surt lifted his flaming sword and flung fire over everything. The sea rose above the mountains and fell crashing over the land. The air trembled, the stars were ripped from the sky as burning earth disappeared under the waves, and the sacred halls of Asgard toppled and fell.

---

[9] the home of the gods and slain heroes

[10] the great wolf that was kept bound by the gods with a magic rope

[11] the earth, regarded as halfway between heaven and hell and encircled by a huge serpent

[12] the great ash tree whose roots and branches held together the universe

---

Norse mythology tells us that the world will end when the forces of evil conquer the forces of good. Write a short essay either agreeing or disagreeing with this prediction and back up your opinion by citing facts and details from real-life observation and your personal experiences.

Many of the selections in this chapter
deal with the human causes of the end
of the world rather than with natural
causes beyond human control. Warfare
has been an almost constant factor in
the course of history.

In "Ragnarokk, The Destiny of the
Gods" war succeeds in destroying
everything—including war. Which then
is worse, a world destroyed by war or a
world that must endure war after war
forever? For James Thurber, there is
the never-ending threat of war, but
always too the everpresent hope of peace
brought about by love.

The Last Flower

James Thurber

World War XII, as everybody knows,
Brought about the collapse of civilization.
Towns, cities, and villages disappeared from the earth.
All the groves and forests were destroyed.
And all the gardens,
And all the works of art.
Men, women, and children became lower than the lower animals.
Discouraged and disillusioned, dogs deserted their fallen masters.
Emboldened by the pitiful condition of the former Lords of the Earth, rabbits
    descended upon them.
Books, paintings, and music disappeared from the earth,
And human beings just sat around, doing nothing.

Years and years went by.
Even the few generals who were left forgot what the last war had decided.
Boys and girls grew up to stare at each other blankly,
For love had passed from the earth.
One day a young girl who had never seen a flower
Chanced to come upon the last one in the world.
She told the other human beings that the last flower was dying.

The only one who paid any attention to her
Was a young man she found wandering about.
Together the young man and the girl nurtured the flower.
And it began to live again.

One day a bee visited the flower, and a hummingbird.
Before long there were two flowers, and then four,
And then a great many groves and forests flourished again.
The young girl began to take an interest in how she looked.
The young man discovered that touching the girl was pleasurable.
Love was reborn into the world.
Their children grew up strong and healthy
And learned to run and laugh.
Dogs came out of their exile.
The young man discovered, by putting one stone upon another,
How to build a shelter.
Pretty soon everybody was building shelters.

Towns, cities, and villages sprang up.
Song came back into the world,
And troubadours and jugglers,
And tailors and cobblers,
And painters and poets,
And sculptors and wheelwrights,
And soldiers. . . .

And lieutenants and captains,
And generals and major generals,
And liberators.
Some people went one place to live,
And some another.
Before long, those who went to live in the valleys
Wished they had gone to live in the hills.
And those who had gone to live in the hills
Wished they had gone to live in the valleys.

The liberators, under the guidance of God,
Set fire to the discontent.
So presently the world was at war again.
This time the destruction was so complete. . . .
That nothing at all was left in the world

Except one man
And one woman
And one flower.

Choose either the first stanza, which lists details of the collapse of civilization, or the third stanza, which lists details of the rebirth of civilization. Continue either list of related events and try to preserve the mood of the poem.

---

1. Disaster, in the form of a nuclear explosion, has struck, but miraculously you are still alive. You are at school and you start walking to your home. What do you see? Write a description of the buildings and other landmarks which you normally pass on your way home. Include also what you imagine you would find as you arrive at home.

2. Reexamine the "big bang" theory of the beginning and ending of the universe as outlined by John W. Clark. Create a poster illustrating the different stages of this process. Include precise captions with your illustrations.

3. The narrator of the selection from *The Time Machine* chose to explore life in the future. If you owned a machine which could travel through time, where would you place it to begin your journey and in which direction in time would you travel? Write a travelogue of the sights you would visit.

4. Write your own myth about the end of the world. Does it go out with a bang, as in "Ragnarokk, The Destiny of the Gods" or with a whimper, as in *The Time Machine*?

5. Write a short letter giving advice to the man and woman in "The Last Flower" who have survived World War XIII. Suggest what they must do to avoid World War XIV.

Activities

6. Study the selections in this chapter to discover which images occur most frequently in describing the end of the world. Then, make up your own image and use it in a short description of the end of the world. For example, "In the end, the world swelled up and burst apart like a tire pumped too full of air."

7. Research some myths about the end of the world. Choose the one that interests you most and prepare an oral report about it for the class. Add a copy of your report to the class Myth Book.

8. Many books deal with the end of the world. Read one from the list below and discuss it with other members of the class who read the same book. As a group, prepare an oral report relating the book to the problems discussed in this chapter.

The Greatest Thing Since Sliced Bread by Don Robertson
Childhood's End by Arthur C. Clarke
Rebirth by John Wyndham
The Last Battle by C. S. Lewis
Hiroshima by John Hersey
On the Beach by Nevil Shute
The Time Machine by H. G. Wells

10
World
Without End

If you examine carefully the "big bang" theory that is described on page 127, you will notice that there is no real end to the universe, since at the moment of complete destruction a new explosion will supposedly occur and the universe will be reborn. This theory of endlessness or cycles in the life of the universe is shared by several religions and philosophies around the world. One symbol that represents such a cycle shows a snake with its tail in its mouth. The snake has a beginning and an end, but at the same time, like a perfect circle, it does not have either.

What kinds of cycles can you think of where beginnings and endings are almost one and the same? Draw a sketch of any cycle that you may be familiar with, such as the cycle of the seasons, the food chain, the cycle of rain and evaporation, the life cycles of insects, or beliefs in reincarnation. Display the sketches on the class bulletin board.

Much of creation seems to be governed by the cycles of the universe. Do these cycles also govern the human body? A clue to the answer comes to a Japanese workman in a letter from a girl which he finds sealed in a wooden box in a barrel of cement.

Letter Found in a Cement-Barrel

Hayama Yoshiki

Matsudo Yoshizō was emptying cement-barrels. He managed to keep the cement off most of his body, but his hair and upper lip were covered by a thick gray coating. He desperately wanted to pick his nose and remove the hardened cement which was making the hairs in his nostrils stand stiff like reinforced concrete; but the cement-mixer was spewing forth ten loads every minute and he could not afford to fall behind in its feeding.

His working day lasted for eleven hours and not once did he have time to pick his nose properly. During his brief lunch break he was hungry and had to concentrate on gulping down food. He had hoped to use the afternoon break for cleaning out his nostrils, but when the time came he found that he had to unclog the cement-mixer instead. By late afternoon his nose felt as if it were made of plaster of Paris.

The day drew to an end. His arms had become limp with exhaustion and he had to exert all his strength to move the barrels. As he started to lift one of them, he noticed a small wooden box lying in the cement.

"What's this?" he wondered vaguely, but he could not let curiosity slow down the pace of his work. Hurriedly he shoveled cement onto the measuring frame, emptied it into the mixing boat, and then began shoveling out more cement again.

"Wait a minute!" he muttered to himself. "Why . . . should there be a box inside a cement-barrel?"

He picked up the box and dropped it into the front pocket of his overalls.

"Doesn't weigh much. . . ! Can't be much money in it, whatever else there is."

Even this slight pause had made him fall behind in his work and now he had to shovel furiously to catch up with the cement-mixer. Like a wild automaton *, he emptied the next barrel and loaded the

---

* robot

contents onto a new measuring frame.

Presently the mixer began to slow down and eventually it came to a stop. It was time for Matsudo Yoshizō to knock off for the day. He picked up the rubber hose that was attached to the mixer and made a preliminary attempt at washing his face and hands. Then he hung his lunch box round his neck and trudged back toward his tenement. His mind was absorbed with the idea of getting some food into his stomach and, even more important, a powerful cup of rice brandy.

He passed the power plant. The construction work was almost finished: soon they would be having electricity. In the distance Mt. Keira towered in the evening darkness with its coat of pure-white snow. The man's sweaty body was suddenly gripped by the cold and he began to shiver. Next to where he walked the rough waters of the Kiso River bit into the milky foam with a barking roar.

. . . "It's too much. Yes, it's too . . . much! The old woman's pregnant again."

He thought of the six children who already squirmed about their tenement room, and of the new child who was going to be born just as the cold season was coming on, and of his wife who seemed to give birth pell-mell to one baby after another; and he was sick at heart.

"Let's see now," he muttered. "They pay me one yen ninety sen a day, and out of that we have to buy two measures of rice at fifty sen each, and then we have to pay out another ninety sen for clothing and a place to live. . . . How do they expect me to have enough left over for a drink?"

Abruptly he remembered the little box in his pocket. He took it out and rubbed it against the seat of his trousers to clean off the cement. Nothing was written on the box. It was securely sealed.

"Now, why . . . should anyone want to seal a box like this? He likes to act mysterious, whoever he is."

He hit the box against a stone, but the lid still would not open. Thoroughly exasperated, he threw it down and stepped on it furiously. The box broke and on the ground lay a scrap of paper wrapped in a rag. He picked it up and read:

"I am a factory girl working for the Nomura Cement Company. I sew cement-bags. My boyfriend used to work for the same company. His job was to put stones into the crusher. Then on the morning of October 7th, just as he was going to put in a big rock, he slipped on the mud and fell into the crusher underneath the rock.

"The other men tried to pull him out, but it was no use. He sank down under the rock, just as if he was being drowned. Then the rock and his body were broken to pieces and came out together from the ejector looking like a big flat pink stone. They fell onto the conveyor belt and were carried into the pulverizer. There they were pounded by the huge steel cylinder. I could hear them screaming out some sort of a spell as they were finally crushed to bits. Then they were put into the burner and baked into a fine slab of cement.

"His bones, his flesh, his mind had all turned into powder. Yes, my boyfriend ended up entirely as cement. All that was left was a scrap of material from his overalls. Today I've been busy sewing the bags into which they'll put him.

"I'm writing this letter the day after he became cement, and when I've finished I'm going to stick it into the bag in this barrel.

"Are you a workman, too? If you are, have a heart and send me an answer. What is the cement in this barrel used for? I very much want to know.

"How much cement did he become? And is it all used in the same place or in different places? Are you a plasterer or a builder?

"I couldn't bear to see him become the corridor of a theater or the wall of some large mansion. But what on earth can I do to stop it? If you are a workman, please don't use the cement in such a place. . . .

"On second thought, though, it doesn't matter. Use it wherever you want. Wherever he's buried, he'll make a good job of it. He's a good solid fellow and he'll do the right thing wherever he happens to end up.

"He had a very gentle nature, you know. But at the same time he was a brave, husky fellow. He was still young. He'd only just turned twenty-five. I never had time to find out how much he really loved me. And here I am sewing a shroud for him—or rather, a cement-bag. Instead of going into a crematorium, he ended up in a rotation kiln. But how shall I find his grave to say goodbye to him? I haven't the faintest idea where he's going to be buried, you see. East or west, far or near—there's no way of telling. That's why I want you to send me an answer. If you're a workman, you will answer me, won't you? And in return I'll give you a piece of cloth from his overalls—yes,

the piece of cloth this letter's wrapped in. The dust from that rock, the sweat from his body—it's all gone into this cloth. The cloth is all that's left of those overalls he used to wear when he embraced me— oh, how hard he used to embrace me!

"Please do this for me, won't you? I know it's a lot of trouble, but please let me know the date when this cement was used, and the sort of place it was used in and the exact address—and also your own name. And you'll be careful too, won't you? Goodbye."

* * *

The din of the children once more surged about Matsudo Yoshizō. He glanced at the name and address at the end of the letter and gulped down the rice brandy that he had poured into a teacup.

"I'm going to drink myself silly!" he shouted. "And I'm going to break every . . . thing I can lay my hands on."

"I see," said his wife. "So you can afford to get drunk, can you? And what about the children?"

He looked at his wife's bloated stomach and remembered his seventh child.

---

1. Write a newspaper article about the factory worker's death. Begin with an eye-catching headline and conclude by speculating about the final "resting place" of the worker's body.

or

2. Outline a story about the romance and unhappy ending of the two cement factory workers. A plot has four basic parts: commencement, conflict, climax, and conclusion. You already have the conclusion given to you. Provide the rest, using only one or two sentences for each plot element.

PEANUTS ®
By Charles M. Schulz

Nothing Gold Can Stay

Robert Frost

Nature's first green is gold,
Her hardest hue to hold.
Her early leaf's a flower;
But only so an hour.
Then leaf subsides to leaf.
So Eden sank to grief,
So dawn goes down to day.
Nothing gold can stay.

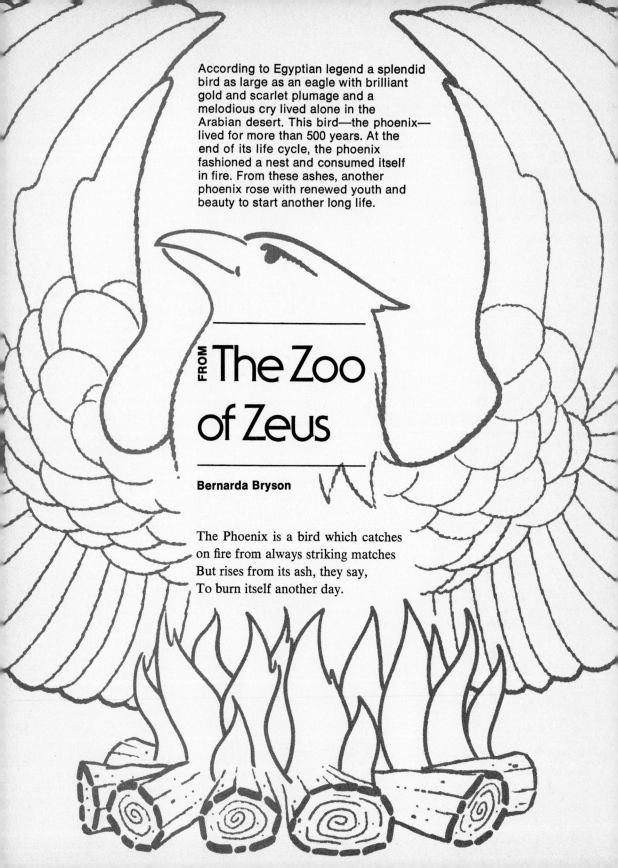

According to Egyptian legend a splendid bird as large as an eagle with brilliant gold and scarlet plumage and a melodious cry lived alone in the Arabian desert. This bird—the phoenix—lived for more than 500 years. At the end of its life cycle, the phoenix fashioned a nest and consumed itself in fire. From these ashes, another phoenix rose with renewed youth and beauty to start another long life.

FROM The Zoo of Zeus

Bernarda Bryson

The Phoenix is a bird which catches
on fire from always striking matches
But rises from its ash, they say,
To burn itself another day.

Mr. Tancred Poldero thought he had a money-making attraction when he acquired a phoenix for his Wizard Wonderworld show. Imagine how much money could be made by selling tickets to witness an event that only happens once every 500 years—the self destruction of the old phoenix and the miraculous birth of the new one from the ashes!

The Phoenix

Sylvia Townsend Warner

Lord Strawberry, a nobleman, collected birds. He had the finest aviary in Europe, so large that eagles did not find it uncomfortable, so well laid out that both humming-birds and snow-buntings had a climate that suited them perfectly. But for many years the finest set of apartments remained empty, with just a label saying: "PHOENIX. *Habitat: Arabia.*"

Many authorities on bird life had assured Lord Strawberry that the phoenix is a fabulous bird, or that the breed was long extinct. Lord Strawberry was unconvinced: his family had always believed in phoenixes. At intervals he received from his agents (together with statements of their expenses) birds which they declared were the phoenix but which turned out to be orioles, macaws, turkey buzzards dyed orange, etc., or stuffed cross-breeds, ingeniously assembled from various plumages. Finally Lord Strawberry went himself to Arabia, where, after some months, he found a phoenix, won its confidence, caught it, and brought it home in perfect condition.

It was a remarkably fine phoenix, with a charming character—affable to the other birds in the aviary and much attached to Lord Strawberry. On its arrival in England it made a great stir among ornithologists, journalists, poets, and milliners, and was constantly visited. But it was not puffed by these attentions, and when it was no longer in the news, and the visits fell off, it showed no pique or rancour. It ate well, and seemed perfectly contented.

It costs a great deal of money to keep up an aviary. When Lord Strawberry died he died penniless. The aviary came on the market. In normal times the rarer birds, and certainly the phoenix, would have been bid for by the trustees of Europe's great zoological societies, or by private persons in the U.S.A.; but as it happened Lord Strawberry died just after a world war, when both money and bird-seed were hard to come by (indeed the cost of bird-seed was one of the things which had ruined Lord Strawberry). The London *Times* urged in a leader that the phoenix be bought for the London Zoo, saying that a nation of bird-lovers had a moral right to own such a rarity; and a fund, called the Strawberry Phoenix Fund, was opened. Students, naturalists, and school-children contributed according to their means; but their means were small, and there were no large donations. So Lord Strawberry's executors (who had the death duties to consider) closed with the higher offer of Mr. Tancred Poldero, owner and proprietor of Poldero's Wizard Wonderworld.

For quite a while Mr. Poldero considered his phoenix a bargain. It was a civil and obliging bird, and adapted itself readily to its new surroundings. It did not cost much to feed, it did not mind children; and though it had no tricks, Mr. Poldero supposed it would soon pick up some. The publicity of the Strawberry Phoenix Fund was now most helpful. Almost every contributor now saved up another half-crown in order to see the phoenix. Others, who had not contributed to the fund, even paid double to look at it on the five-shilling days.

But then business slackened. The phoenix was as handsome as ever, and as amiable; but, as Mr. Poldero said, it hadn't got Udge. Even at popular prices the phoenix was not really popular. It was too quiet, too classical. So people went instead to watch the antics of the baboons, or to admire the crocodile who had eaten the woman.

One day Mr. Poldero said to his manager, Mr. Ramkin:

"How long since any fool paid to look at the phoenix?"

"Matter of three weeks," replied Mr. Ramkin.

"Eating his head off," said Mr. Poldero. "Let alone the insurance. Seven shillings a week it costs me to insure that bird, and I might as well insure the Arch-bishop of Canterbury."

"The public don't like him. He's too quiet for them, that's the trouble. Won't mate nor nothing. And I've tried him with no end of pretty pollies, ospreys, and Cochin-Chinas, and the Lord knows what. But he won't look at them."

"Wonder if we could swap him for a livelier one," said Mr. Poldero.

"Impossible. There's only one of him at a time."

"Go on!"

"I mean it. Haven't you ever read what it says on the label?"

They went to the phoenix's cage. It flapped its wings politely, but they paid no attention. They read:

"PANSY. *Phoenix phoenixissima for-mosissima arabiana.* This rare and fabu-lous bird is UNIQUE. The World's Old Bachelor. Has no mate and doesn't want one. When old, sets fire to itself and emerges miraculously reborn. Specially imported from the East."

"I've got an idea," said Mr. Poldero. "How old do you suppose that bird is?"

"Looks in its prime to me," said Mr. Ramkin.

"Suppose," continued Mr. Poldero, "we could somehow get him alight? We'd advertise it beforehand, of course, work up interest. Then we'd have a new bird, and a bird with some romance about it, a bird with a life-story. We could sell a bird like that."

Mr. Ramkin nodded.

"I've read about it in a book," he said. "You've got to give them scented woods and what not, and they build a nest and sit down on it and catch fire spontaneous. But they won't do it till they're old. That's the snag."

"Leave that to me," said Mr. Poldero. "You get those scented woods, and I'll do the ageing."

It was not easy to age the phoenix. Its allowance of food was halved, and halved again, but though it grew thinner its eyes

CAROL WALD

were undimmed and its plumage glossy as ever. The heating was turned off; but it puffed out its feathers against the cold, and seemed none the worse. Other birds were put into its cage, birds of a peevish and quarrelsome nature. They pecked and chivied it; but the phoenix was so civil and amiable that after a day or two they lost their animosity. Then Mr. Poldero tried alley cats. These could not be won by manners, but the phoenix darted above their heads and flapped its golden wings in their faces, and daunted them.

Mr. Poldero turned to a book on Arabia, and read that the climate was dry. "Aha!" said he. The phoenix was moved to a small cage that had a sprinkler in the ceiling. Every night the sprinkler was turned on. The phoenix began to cough. Mr. Poldero had another good idea. Daily he stationed himself in front of the cage to jeer at the bird and abuse it.

When spring was come, Mr. Poldero felt justified in beginning a publicity campaign about the ageing phoenix. The old public favourite, he said, was nearing its end. Meanwhile he tested the bird's reactions every few days by putting a few tufts of foul-smelling straw and some strands of rusty barbed wire into the cage, to see if it were interested in nesting yet. One day the phoenix began turning over the straw. Mr. Poldero signed a contract for the film rights. At last the hour seemed ripe. It was a fine Saturday evening in May. For some weeks the public interest in the ageing phoenix had been working up, and the admission charge had risen to five shillings. The enclosure was thronged. The lights and the cameras were trained on the cage, and a loud-speaker proclaimed to the audience the rarity of what was about to take place.

"The phoenix," said the loud-speaker, "is the aristocrat of bird-life. Only the rarest and most expensive specimens of oriental wood, drenched in exotic perfumes, will tempt him to construct his strange love-nest."

Now a neat assortment of twigs and shavings, strongly scented, was shoved into the cage.

"The phoenix," the loud-speaker continued, "is as capricious as Cleopatra, as luxurious as la du Barry, as heady as a strain of wild gypsy music. All the fantastic pomp and passion of the ancient East, its languorous magic, its subtle cruelties . . ."

"Lawks!" cried a woman in the crowd. "He's at it!"

A quiver stirred the dulled plumage. The phoenix turned its head from side to side. It descended, staggering, from its perch. Then wearily it began to pull about the twigs and shavings.

The cameras clicked, the lights blazed full on the cage. Rushing to the loud-speaker Mr. Poldero exclaimed:

"Ladies and gentlemen, this is the thrilling moment the world has breathlessly awaited. The legend of centuries is materializing before our modern eyes. The phoenix . . ."

The phoenix settled on its pyre and appeared to fall asleep.

The film director said:

"Well, if it doesn't evaluate more than this, mark it instructional."

At that moment the phoenix and the pyre burst into flames. The flames streamed upwards, leaped out on every side. In a minute or two everything was burned to ashes, and some thousand people, including Mr. Poldero, perished in the blaze.

Design a flyer, bumper sticker, or newspaper advertisement for Mr. Poldero to use to attract customers to his Wizard Wonderworld.

Is phoenixlike rebirth possible in human terms? Claire Myers Owens records her own personal experience when in a mystical and ecstatic moment she was reborn.

I Was Reborn!

Claire Myers Owens

Suddenly the entire room was filled with a great golden light, the whole world was filled with nothing but light. There was nothing anywhere except this effulgent light and my own small kernel of the self. The ordinary "I" ceased to exist. Nothing of me remained but a mere nugget of consciousness. It felt as if some vast transcendent force was invading me without my volition, as if all the immanent good lying latent within me began to pour forth in a stream, to form a moving circle with the universal principle. Myself began to dissolve into the light that was like a great golden all-pervasive fog. It was a mystical moment of union with the cosmic principle. I felt at one with the mysterious infinite, with all things, all people. It was a confrontation with Ultimate Reality, an overwhelming indescribable experience, the ecstasy so intense it was unbearable, the rapture so sweet it was ineffable.

I WAS REBORN.

One kind of rebirth is a spiritual rebirth in which a person can erase past mistakes and begin a new life. Write a page or two beginning, "If I could live my life over again, I would. . . ."

Most people delight in the never-ending
changes of the seasons. Yet in their
changing there is permanence, because
the seasons follow a predictable pattern.
In a sense, they are like the phoenix—
changing but changeless. "A Wheel of
Seasons" describes this "perfect
symbol" of rebirth.

A Wheel of Seasons

William Vincent Sieller

Here lies the perfect symbol, quiet now
And resting from its journeys, mile on mile;
The whirling race is done, but time is slow
In weathering a flattened wagon wheel.
Within a circle, lying on the ground,
Twelve spokes divide twelve plots of grass and weed
In formal gardens, segments in the round
Now measuring a different kind of speed.
Each spring can find the pattern soon enough,
But summer growth will hide the curving edge,
And autumn leaves will fall for winds to scuff
Till winter snows have covered every wedge.
The inner part, the hub, the core of change,
Holds seasons fanning from its central hinge.

**The poem describes a wagon wheel lying flat on the
ground in the middle of a garden. In your own words
tell how the wagon wheel can be taken as the "perfect
symbol" for the changing seasons.**

Within the cycles of the seasons there is time to rejoice in all the works of humankind.

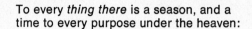

To every *thing there* is a season, and a
time to every purpose under the heaven:

A time to be born, and a time to die;
a time to plant, and a time to pluck up
that which is planted;

A time to kill, and a time to heal; a
time to break down, and a time to build
up;

A time to weep, and a time to laugh;
a time to mourn, and a time to dance;

A time to cast away stones, and a
time to gather stones together; a time
to embrace, and a time to refrain from
embracing;

A time to get, and a time to lose; a
time to keep, and a time to cast away;

A time to rend, and a time to sew; a
time to keep silence, and a time to
speak;

A time to love, and a time to hate; a
time of war, and a time of peace.

Wherefore I perceive that *there is*
nothing better, than that a man should
rejoice in his own works; for that *is* his
portion: for who shall bring him to see
what shall be after him?

Ecclesiastes (3: 1–8, 22)

Aztec calendar, carved in a stone
weighing over 20 tons, from the Pyramid
of the Sun, Mexico City. The Aztecs
begin to appear in history at about 1100
A.D., but this calendar covers the whole
previous history of the world.

**Following the pattern of verses
2–8, compose several verses that
could be added to Ecclesiastes to
illustrate that "to everything there
is a season." Note that a pair of
opposite ideas are used here to
make up each unit of thought.**

Examine the illustrations that appear on these pages. Write an interesting caption for each picture, revealing how it represents both a beginning and an end to something.

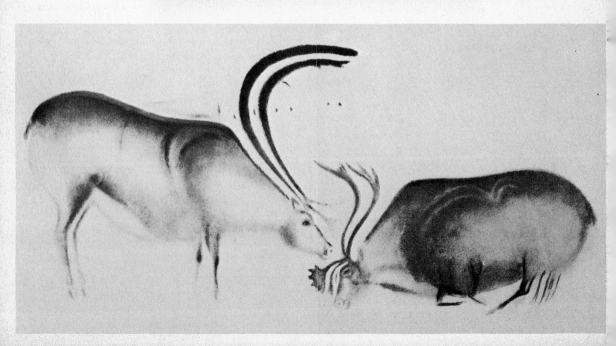

153

1. Write the letter which Matsudo Yoshizō will write to the factory girl in "Letter Found in a Cement-Barrel." Be sure to include all of the information that the girl requested in her letter.

Activities

2. In "Ragnarokk, The Destiny of the Gods," Yggdrasil is the world tree whose roots and branches hold together the universe. In the Peanuts cartoon, the tree symbolizes the passage of time. What other things can a tree symbolize? Think of holidays, flags, and insignias on which trees play an important part. List them, and after each indicate why you think the symbol of the tree is used.

3. The Bible tells of two trees in the Garden of Eden. One was the tree of knowledge of good and evil from which Eve plucked the forbidden fruit. The other was the tree of life. A family tree is a symbol of life as well. Check with relatives to determine the extent of your family tree. After checking how a family tree is usually constructed, draw a representation of your family tree.

4. You are one of Mr. Tancred Poldero's employees and you are outraged by his mistreatment of the phoenix. Write a letter to the Society for the Prevention of Cruelty to Animals, reporting this mistreatment and suggesting steps to be taken to protect such a valuable bird as the phoenix.

5. (a) Mr. Tancred Poldero has bought commercial time on television to promote the big moment when the phoenix will build its nest and burn itself. He has paid for one minute. Write the script.

or

(b) If videotape equipment is available in your school, direct the shooting of Mr. Poldero's commercial. If several are taped, play the recorded commercials for the class, who will decide which is the most effective.

6. With a group of classmates, explore the theory of reincarnation. Prepare an oral report in which you present the evidence which is used to support the theory. Books and authors which you may consider reading are: *The Search for Bridey Murphy* by Morey Bernstein, *We Have Lived Before* by Brad Steiger, and books by or about Ruth Montgomery, Jeane Dixon, Arthur Ford, Edgar Cayce, and Eileen Garrett.

7. Research the subject of calendars and write a report explaining how the twelve-month calendar came into being. Include a brief summary of calendars that are no longer used.

8. Reexamine the topics discussed in each chapter of this book. Pay particular attention to Chapter Four, in which you studied the major events in a person's life. Write a summarizing paper in which you draw your own conclusions regarding the beginnings and endings of you, both as an individual and as a member of the human race.

Inc., 122. "The End of the World" from "The Hollow Men" in *Collected Poems* 1909-1962 by T. S. Eliot. Copyright 1936 by Harcourt Brace Jovanovich, Inc., copyright © 1963, 1964 by T. S. Eliot. Reprinted by permission of the publishers, 125. "The End of the World" *from Collected Poems 1917-1952* by Archibald MacLeish. Reprinted by permission of Houghton Mifflin Company, 126. "The Big Bang Theory" by John W. Clark. Copyright © 1972 by Barbara Dodds Stanford and Gene Stanford. Reprinted by permission of Washington Square Press, a division of Simon and Schuster, Inc., 127. "Fire and Ice" by Robert Frost. From *The Poetry of Robert Frost,* edited by Edward Connery Lathem. Copyright 1916, 1923, © 1969 by Holt, Rinehart and Winston, Inc. Copyright 1944, 1951 by Robert Frost. Reprinted by permission of Holt, Rinehart and Winston, Inc., 131. "Ragnarokk, The Destiny of the Gods" from *Norse Gods and Giants,* copyright © 1967 by Ingri and Edgar Parin d'Aulaire. Reprinted by permission of Doubleday and Company, Inc., 132. From *The Last Flower,* by James Thurber. Copyright © 1939 James Thurber. © 1967 Helen W. Thurber and Rosemary Thurber Sauers from *The Last Flower* published by Harper & Row, Publishers, 134. "Letter Found in a Cement-Barrel," by Hayama Yoshiki pg. 204, from *Modern Japanese Stories,* edited by Ivan Morris. Reprinted by permission of Charles E. Tuttle Co., Inc., 140. "Nothing Gold Can Stay" by Robert Frost. From *The Poetry of Robert Frost,* edited by Edward Connery Lathem. Copyright 1916, 1923, © 1969 by Holt, Rinehart and Winston, Inc. Copyright 1944, 1951 by Robert Frost. Reprinted by permission of Holt, Rinehart and Winston, Inc., 143. From *The Zoo of Zeus* by Bernarda Bryson. All rights reserved. Reprinted by permission of Grossman Publishers, 144. "The Phoenix" by Sylvia Townsend Warner. From THE CAT'S CRADLE by Sylvia Townsend Warner, Copyright 1940, Copyright © renewed 1968 by Sylvia Townsend Warner. Reprinted by permission of The Viking Press, 145. "I Was Reborn" from *Awakening to the Good* by Claire Myers Owens. Reprinted by permission of the author, 149. "A Wheel of Seasons" by William Vincent Sieller. Originally appeared in the *Christian Science Monitor.* Reprinted by permission of the author and *The Golden Quill Press,* 150.

Picture Credits

key: NYPL = New York Public Library Picture Collection

Page 2 – Sunburst pieced quilt, 1865, courtesy "America Hurrah" Antiques; from "The Quilt Engagement Calendar", E. P. Dutton, N. Y. (1975); 5 – Culver; 7 – William Blake, "The Ancient of Days Striking the First Circle of the Earth" (detail); 10 – "Cosmic Lion Goddess" (detail) from 18th cent. Indian illuminated ms., The Pierpont Morgan Library; 11 – "God Creating the Animals", (detail) from the illuminated French Bible of Holkam Hall, England, 14th cent., The British Museum; 12 – "Adam and Eve", Swedish Folk Art, Nordiska Museet, Stockholm; 14 – NASA; 17 – Detail from Queen Anne Wing Chair, 18th cent., The Metropolitan Museum of Art; 23 – "Adam and Eve" by Kalender, Turkish, 17th cent., courtesy The Tapkapu Museum, Istanbul; 24 – American Museum of Natural History; 27 – Culver; 31 – Birth Certificate of Johannes Stumpf, 1788 by Johann Zug, Lancaster Co., Pa. (NYPL); 32 – Chris Reeberg, DPI; 37 – "Birth of Christ", Swedish Folk Art, Nordiska Museet, Stockholm; 39 – Roy Pinney, Monkmeyer; 41 – A. W. Ambler, Audubon/Photo Researchers; 42 – "Stairs of Ages", Swedish Folk Art, Nordiska Museet, Stockholm; 44 – From Grandma Moses' "My Life's History", 1952, edited by Otto Kallir, reprinted by permission of Harper and Row, New York; 48 – "Jack and the Beanstalk" from "The Green Fairy Book", edited by Andrew Lang, Dover; 51 – "Excalibur the Sword" by Howard Pyle; 59 – Mark Haven; 69 – Culver; 70, 71 – NYPL; 72 – Anon., "Polly Botsford and Her Children, c.1813", Mourning Picture, Abbey Aldrich Rockefeller Collection of American Folk Art; 80 – Trans World Airlines; 84 – NYPL; 86 – Jim Jowers, Nancy Palmer Photo Agency; 87 – American Museum of Natural History; 88 – Alfred Eisentaedt, Time/Life Picture Agency; 91, 96 – Vivian Berger; 99 – From "Devils, Demons, Death and Damnation" by E. & J. Lehner (Dover); 104 – Bowl of Fruit, painted on velvet, Wisconsin, 1850, NYPL Picture Collection; 106 – Constantine Manos, Magnum; 111, 113 – Carol Wald; 115 – Russ Kinne, Photo Researchers; 119 – Primitive Farm Scene, 18th cent. Garbisch Collection, National Gallery of Art, Washington, D. C.; 125 – "Angel Gabriel", anon., New England, c.1840, ht. 29¼", Museum of American Folk Art; 126 – Alexander Calder, "Lion Tamer", 1932, pen and ink, 12½" x 14", The Philadelphia Museum; 128, 129 – Werner Stoy, DPI; 130 – Horst Schafer, Photo Trends; 135 – © 1943, James Thurber; © 1971, Helen W. Thurber and Rosemary Thurber Sauers, from "Men, Woman and Dogs", Harcourt Brace Jovanovich; originally published in The New Yorker Magazine; 137 – Civil Defense Administration; 138 – Patchwork Quilt, Mariner's Compass, c.1860, Philadelphia, (Phyllis Haders) from "The Quilt Engagement Calendar", E. P. Dutton, N. Y. (1975); 142 – Rhoda Galyn; 14 – © 1959, United Features Syndicate; 147 – Carol Wald; 149 – NYPL; 151 – National Museum of Anthropology, Mexico City; 152 – (t) Culver; (b) French Government Tourist Office; 153 – (t) NASA; (b) U.S. Dept. of Interior; 57, 75, 77, 79, 82, 102 – From "Early New England Gravestone Rubbings" by Edmund Vincent Gillon, Jr., Dover.

Mechanicals by John Lind Corp.

Cover Photography by Arthur Tress.